The Complete Book of
Vine Growing
in the British Isles

The
Complete Book of
Vine Growing
in the British Isles

Jack Ward

faber and faber
LONDON · BOSTON

First published in 1984
by Faber and Faber Limited
3 Queen Square London WC1N 3AU
Filmset by Wilmaset, Birkenhead, Merseyside
Printed in Great Britain by
Redwood Burn Ltd.,
Trowbridge, Wiltshire
All rights reserved

© Jack Ward, 1984

British Library Cataloguing in Publication Data

Ward, Jack
The complete book of vine growing in the British
Isles.
1. Viticulture—Great Britain
I. Title
634'.8'0941   SB397.G7

ISBN 0-571-13257-X

Contents

Illustrations

Preface

Whatever might be the Cause of this total Neglect in cultivating Vines in England, I will not pretend to determine; but such was the Prejudice most People conceived to any Attempts of producing Wine in England, that, for some Ages past, every Trial of that kind has been ridiculed by the Generality of People; and at this day very few persons will believe it possible to be effected.

Indeed, if we judge only by the Success of some modern Essays made near London, where small Vineyards have been planted a few Years past, there would be no great Encouragement to begin a Work of this kind, because the Produce of very few of these Vineyards has been so kindly as were to be wished. But, however, this should not deter others from making further Trials, especially when they consider the many Disadvantages which most or all of these Plantations are attended with: for first, there is scarce one of them placed upon a proper Soil and Situation for this Purpose; and, secondly, there is not one which is rightly planted and managed, as I shall presently shew: and how can we expect Success from Vineyards under these Disadvantages, when even in France or Italy they would succeed little better, if their Management were not directed with more Judgement?

Philip Miller FRS, *The Gardeners Dictionary*, London, 1748

Anyone wishing to grow vines in the United Kingdom must ensure they are 'rightly planted and managed' if he wants to succeed. The French, who appear to be favoured with a much better climate, can afford to step out of line when it suits their convenience, but the British, with their hostile weather conditions, must pay closer attention to the principles of viticulture and satisfy them whenever they can. Philip Miller, were he alive today, would probably make the same comment as he did in 1748. Vineyards in England today are often to be found on inappropriate sites; some have even been planted on unsuitable soils and are frequently stocked with the wrong varieties.

But before condemning the inexperience of English growers, it might be wise to remember that the technical skills of vine growing vary from country to country and even from district to district. It may be fair to say that conditions in Luxemburg and the Moselle valley, on the northern perimeter of the wine-growing belt, must be roughly the same as those prevailing in southern England and therefore we should follow their viticultural practices rather than copy those of the French; at the same time we must never forget that we live on an island and enjoy a maritime climate, with all the benefits and hazards that are likely to ensue.

Some experimental work is therefore needed if any progress is to be made and, provided certain basic principles are not forgotten, should be undertaken by as many English growers as possible. Viticulturists all over the world have been obliged to adapt the practices of other countries in order to obtain the best results. Great Britain so far has not had much time to indulge in this kind of research.

It is thus quite significant to find that some English growers have preferred American techniques to the more established and orthodox European methods. Geneva Double Curtain for instance, has achieved a measure of success in the United Kingdom, particularly when poor summers have rendered the Guyot system unproductive. It has never been established however whether this success has been caused by longer exposure to sunlight, a bonus which inevitably results from wider spacing. With more than 2,000 vines to the acre, standard Guyot practices may produce overcrowding in this country, where sunshine is not as plentiful as it should be. The generous leaf canopy, so favoured by the experts, could throw a certain amount of shade during the day and, in a miserable summer, affect the fruit buds for the following year. If this is the case, it would be better to space the rows further apart; evidence already seems to show that heavier yields will result if such measures are taken.

The survival of English viticulture will depend almost entirely on the ability to maintain an adequate yield per acre. At a relatively modest level this can still be viable, provided the vineyard is not too small. Nevertheless the average at present achieved is scarcely sufficient, if the cultivation of vines is to be regarded as a profitable undertaking. More effort should therefore be made to increase the yield by choosing suitable varieties and following the basic principles of good husbandry.

It has often been maintained that quantity can be achieved only at the expense of quality. This is largely true and is a fact that must be duly considered in other countries but, for the English grower, the same rules do not fully apply. The European Economic Community does not permit us to produce quality wines or, at any rate, to describe them as such. If we are therefore condemned to produce table wines exclusively, we should aim for quantity rather than quality; after all that is what many of our competitors on the other side of the Channel are prepared to do. It is clearly more profitable to produce two bottles of good English wine than strive to achieve one of superior quality, for which nobody will be ready to pay double the price.

In no way does this mean that quality should be disregarded. Indeed, there is little evidence to show that wines produced in England are appreciably inferior to those imported from abroad. There are plenty of people capable of making drinkable table wines in this country, even from musts of comparatively low gravity. On the other hand, they will not be able to make wine of any sort, if the grapes are not there.

Anyone who wants to grow vines in the United Kingdom must be prepared to accept failure in certain years. This will mean some degree of financial flexibility and an ability to survive the lean harvests. Nevertheless a great deal can be done by careful planning, good husbandry and clever marketing to make the English vineyard commercially viable.

Most vignerons today still talk in terms of feet, inches, acres and tons, so their practice has been followed in this book, and metric units have been used only where scientific usage or Continental custom requires them.

J.L.W.
May 1983

1

The Vineyard Environment

The Site

For those who have the choice, it is very important to find a suitable site and particularly so here in England, where vines will need all the help they can get. The classic position of course is on a south-facing slope, where the sun at midday is shining vertically overhead. If this is not possible, it is better to choose land inclining to the West rather than to the East. Agricultural land at the right altitude is usually flat in Britain, except where abundant rainfall would be likely to encourage botrytis and other fungous diseases. This is a pity, because a sloping vineyard, although more difficult to manage, has a natural capacity for drainage. If the perfect site can eventually be found, it is often not possible to use it for the cultivation of vines.

Whether or not the aspect of a vineyard is ideal, there are certain other features that ought to be considered. Although vines are cultivated in the Alps at altitudes of well over 1,000 feet, the English would be unwise to expect satisfactory results at this sort of level. Ray Barrington Brock used to maintain that he could ripen fruit at Oxted, where the altitude exceeded 400 feet; it has nevertheless been established that the length of the growing season can be adversely affected by the height of a vineyard above sea-level.

A hilly site is less likely to be damaged by a May frost, provided the cold air has a chance to escape from the bottom of the slope; on flat ground the problem is more acute and steps should be taken to ascertain whether the prospective vineyard is in a well-known frost pocket.

It is also unwise to choose an area close to the sea. Onshore winds can carry salt up to a distance of 2 miles and damage has already been caused to vineyards planted in Wales and the Isle of Wight. Any site in Britain endowed with natural protection from the wind should be favourably considered. Whether this is provided by some physical feature or is due to the proximity of trees is of little consequence, although a wood can afford valuable cover for predatory birds. The Germans know this and all their northern vineyards are to be found in the clefts of deep river valleys such as the Rhine, the Moselle, the Nahe and the Ahr.

It is well known that the vine prefers a relatively dry atmosphere, without too much humidity. In southern England the incidence of rainfall increases quite dramatically as you go from East to West. The subtropical warmth and abundant rainfall in Devon and Cornwall is in vivid contrast to the drier parts of East Anglia, which suffer periodic exposure to the cold north-east winds. Wet weather accelerates the growth of fungous diseases, so areas with appreciably more than 30 inches of rain in the year should be avoided. The control of botrytis for instance is considerably less expensive and laborious if the ambient conditions are unlikely to encourage its development.

Finally let it be understood that an English vineyard situated close to a main road or in a tourist area will be able to enjoy a great marketing advantage. Vines are a novelty in Britain and will be for many years to come. Growers who realize this will make it their business to cater for visitors and may find it possible to sell their wares at full retail price, instead of having to offer them at a discount through the normal trade channels.

Soil

The vine has been found to grow on soils that range from gravel and sand to quite heavy clays. It is widely believed and certainly true that the plant will often flourish on land which has proved unfit for other crops. That does not mean that a vineyard can be permanently starved, nor does it mean that a fertile site is going to be unsuitable.

Vitis vinifera varieties are deep-rooted if favourable conditions prevail, so it is important to determine the depth of topsoil available and the nature of the subsoil. Their roots are able to penetrate the ground by more than 6 feet if they are unimpeded. Perhaps this is why continental vineyards are initially ploughed to a considerable depth, especially in hot countries where the roots must search diligently for an adequate supply of water. A shallow soil is unlikely to support a heavy yield but could well be responsible for the production of better quality wines.

Nevertheless the actual condition of the soil matters more than its depth or fertility. Ideally it should be porous and friable, admitting air to the roots and, above all, allowing any surplus water to drain away easily. Heavy clays are not very suitable; quite apart from anything else they tend to be cold and sticky, causing the roots to become asphyxiated and unable to perform their proper functions.

In the United Kingdom, which is officially immune from the phylloxera scourge, it is still possible to plant rooted cuttings, provided they are not taken from protected varieties. This could have significance for the English grower choosing a site in the South of England where large areas of chalk abound, for it has been established that *vinifera* varieties are able to tolerate a larger percentage of lime than their American cousins. By crossing *V. berlandieri* with *V. vinifera* it has been possible to evolve rootstocks that will tolerate 40 per cent of chalk in the soil; on land containing an even higher proportion, it might be worth planting *vinifera* varieties on their own roots.

Soil is composed of a variety of particles derived from different sources. Some of it has been caused by the continued action of the climate working on the geological formations of the earth's crust, providing important minerals that are essential for plant growth; some of it is organic matter produced by the decay of vegetation and the excreta of living creatures. Wind and water have been instrumental in broadcasting these particles, creating soils of varying depth and divergent nature.

Soils are usually referred to as being light or heavy and depend for their description on the proportions of sand, silt or clay with which they are formed. A typical vineyard soil may consist of a mixture of these ingredients together with a percentage of organic material. Loam, combined with sand or silt, is likely to have a generous pore space, which means plenty of aeration and an ability to retain sufficient water after drainage to enable the vines to absorb the necessary nutrients. Too much sand on the one hand or too much clay on the other would either restrict growth through lack of moisture or paralyse the roots by asphyxiation. Both soils are likely to benefit from applications of humus, which will improve the pore space by encouraging worms and micro-organisms to become active. In order to maintain bacterial activity in the soil, it is important to remember that organic matter must be repeatedly added, in order to preserve the right kind of texture.

A good soil should be uncompacted in order to allow the roots of the vine to penetrate easily and absorb the nutrients required for the season's growth and production of fruit. For a vineyard a well-drained loam containing about 40 per cent sand, 40 per cent silt and 20 per cent clay would be the kind of soil to choose.

It is sometimes possible to find such conditions existing in a topsoil of insufficient depth over an impenetrable subsoil. In such cases deep ploughing is essential, in order to break up the hard pan before the vines are planted. This may be of greater significance in warmer countries, where the summer rainfall is less abundant. A heavy clay subsoil on the other hand tends to encourage waterlogging and if this occurs during the vegetative period, the vineyard will suffer accordingly. It is wise to dig a short trench to a depth of 3 feet in order to determine whether such a restriction exists.

It has been found by experience that soil compaction is frequently caused by too much cultivation. The use of machinery on the land should be confined to periods when the soil is not too wet and not too dry. Most textbooks recommend the use of a subsoiler capable of breaking up the ground to a depth of 3 feet before any vines are planted, but much will depend on the nature of the land and the uniformity of the soil. The whole object of the exercise is to increase the pore space, permitting water and air freely to penetrate the area occupied by the roots of the plant. As soon as the ground has been properly prepared and planting has taken place, the soil is best left alone. Some growers like to grass their vineyards, using herbicides beneath the trellis work, while others prefer to rely on worms and other living organisms to do their cultivation for them, by applying mulches of compost or farmyard manure.

Soils can be more or less divided into seven categories: sand, loamy sand, sandy loam, loam, clay loam, loamy clay and clay. For the purposes of more accurate identification, a distinction can be made between sand and silt with a further subdivision between coarse and fine sand.

Sandy soils warm quickly and dry out more readily, while clay remains cold and wet. Finer particles of soil have a greater available water capacity. Such considerations are important when assessing the value of a prospective vineyard site.

Rain

In England, south of a line drawn from the mouth of the Severn to the Wash, the average annual rainfall varies from 20 inches (508 mm) in Cambridgeshire, to 90 inches (2,286 mm) on Dartmoor. In Wales the rainfall is even heavier, reaching 175 inches (4,445 mm) in the Snowdon area.

East Anglia is the driest part of the country; in addition to Cambridgeshire there are areas in Bedford, Suffolk and Essex where the volume of rain is scarcely enough to create conditions unfavourable for viticulture. Devon and Cornwall however, which lie at gentler latitudes, get rather too much rain, certainly enough to make the cultivation of vines more difficult. Wet weather encourages fungous disease, particularly if it comes at the wrong time of year and, if accompanied by low temperatures at flowering time, can have a devastating effect on the yield of fruit.

It can be said therefore that, on average, the annual rainfall should not exceed 30 inches (762 mm) and, during the growing period, should ideally remain below 14 inches (say 350 mm). It does not follow however that vines cannot be successfully cultivated in areas where the rainfall is higher. In parts of Germany, for example, some vineyards are obliged to endure up to 40 inches of rain as an annual average but manage to survive, in spite of the extra labour required to resist peronospora and botrytis.

Winter rainfall is of minor importance and during the spring frequent showers help to encourage healthy growth, particularly when accompanied by sunny intervals. Rain can cause damage at flowering time, especially if the weather is cold, and is very unwelcome when the fruit begins to ripen, by adversely affecting the sugar content and increasing the risk of botrytis.

Lack of rain, a symptom not often experienced in Britain, can also be damaging. In 1976 drought was a significant feature of the European summer and aircraft reported the healthy appearance of many English vineyards compared with the surrounding countryside; the vine in its natural habitat is accustomed to arid conditions. Be that as it may, the lack of rain arrested growth and development at a critical time of the year and interfered with the processes required for the natural production of fruit. Ideally rainfall should occur at convenient intervals and at the most favourable periods of the year; to rely on such patterns of climatic behaviour would be optimistic indeed.

Temperature

Sunshine and rainfall, together with shelter from the wind, play an important part in the growth and development of a vineyard. Even more significant is the degree of warmth available, particularly at certain times of the year. Too much heat must be avoided and in hot countries some modification can often be achieved by planting vines at a greater altitude. It therefore stands to reason that in colder climates cultivation should be established closer to sea-level.

Much will depend on latitude. The French maintain that vineyards cannot be viable beyond the fiftieth parallel; that eliminates the whole of England with the exception of Lizard Point and the Scilly Isles. The Germans are prepared to concede another degree of latitude and justify their claim by demonstrating the success of their river valleys, the Rhine, the Moselle and the Ahr. Such massive columns of water create their own microclimate and it is natural to think that the Thames valley might be included in the same category in spite of being further north.

An average yearly temperature of at least 9 °C (48 °F) is considered to be essential. England, south of a line drawn from Bristol to the Wash, can maintain an annual temperature of at least 10 °C (50 °F). Yet it must always be remembered that the temperate climate enjoyed by England tends to create warmer winters and colder summers. It is therefore not altogether surprising to find that continental vineyards can register higher temperatures during the growing season, at those critical times when warmth is highly desirable. At flowering time, for instance, the fruit is unlikely to set if the weather is cold and temperatures that fall below 14.5 °C (58 °F) can produce only meagre harvests.

The Americans insist that the success of a vineyard will depend largely on the ambient temperature created by its microclimate. They call it heat summation or degree days and their calculations are based on the assumption that temperatures below 10 °C (50 °F) are unable to produce any vegetative growth in vines. Such being the case, only the degrees registered above 10 °C (50 °F) can be taken into account when estimating the potential of a vineyard. Degree days are sometimes determined from the time of flowering but are more often reckoned from bud burst, terminating with the time of harvest. The formula can be described as follows.

An average temperature for each day must be calculated in the usual way. From the results that emerge, 10 °C (50 °F) should be subtracted for the reasons given above. The sum of all the figures obtained will give the degree days or heat summation for the period concerned. Estimates are more often determined by taking the mean temperature (less 10 °C) for each calendar month of the growing season and multiplying this by the number of days it contains.

Based on a thirty year record, the average monthly temperatures for southern England are as follows:–

May: 11.7 °C (53.06 °F); June: 14.7 °C (58.46 °F); July: 16.4 °C (61.52 °F); August: 16.3 °C (61.36 °F); September: 14.5 °C (58.1 °F); October: 11.3 °C (52.34 °F). This gives a heat summation of 762 (1373) degree days which, according to the experts, will not be enough to ripen the fruit. If that were so, the prospect of growing grapes in the United Kingdom would be bleak indeed. Perhaps it might be comforting to observe that Geisenheim, in the German Rheingau, can, according to authoritative sources, muster only 932 (1709) degree days, a figure which is also considered to be inadequate.

Wind and Windbreaks

Great Britain is an island and a windswept one at that. No vineyard planted in this country will be very far from the sea, so it is safe to assume that it will be dominated by a maritime climate. To the West there lies an ocean and from that quarter come the prevailing winds frequently laden with rain. If the wind blows from the East it is often cold and may be coming from Siberia. Perhaps it is fair to say that there are not many days during the average English summer without at least a gentle breeze.

Quite apart from the damage caused by wind and rain at flowering time, it is well to remember that even a breeze can dilute the intensity of the sun. Strong winds can make it feel cold, or at least colder than would seem apparent from the thermometer. If human beings react in this way, plants should respond in a similar fashion and the incidence of wind in the United Kingdom must be the most important factor in the success of an English harvest.

The effect of the wind has not been underestimated in other wine-producing countries, particularly those which depend on favourable climatic conditions to ripen their grapes. The Germans and the Luxemburgers, with the most northerly vineyards on the Continent, have found suitable river valleys, where adequate protection is afforded by steep slopes, providing maximum heat from the sun. Vines are planted in the hilly country surrounding the rivers Moselle, Saar, Ruwer, Ahr and Rhine. They are not to be found near the summits but are tucked away in the valleys, making the most of what natural protection is available.

In Britain many vineyards have been planted on windy plains or in other exposed places and suffer accordingly when conditions are poor. Fruit farmers are well aware of this problem and protect their more sensitive crops with well-established windbreaks 30 or 40 feet high. From the meagre experience so far available it has been observed that vineyards in England that are surrounded by forest trees usually avoid coulure when the wind blows cold at flowering time. As a result of this protection the whole season is advanced, from bud burst to harvest, and the yield is substantially improved. It has been established furthermore that vines close to a windbreak or hedge fare better than those at a distance; the amount of fruit produced is gradually reduced as the range of protection peters out.

It is therefore important first of all to choose a site with plenty of natural shelter from the wind. A brick wall will never do this as effectively as a row of trees, which acts as a filter and therefore reduces the force of the wind within an area determined by their density and height. Any gaps in the protective barrier should be dealt with as soon as possible. For those obliged to use an exposed site, it is important to plant a collection of suitable trees to act as a windbreak before placing an order for vines.

The exact choice will depend on the location. Some trees, conifers especially, must not be planted too close to the vineyard because they tend to rob the soil of nutrients; others, like Italian alders, are said to be innocuous, even to make a contribution. Whatever varieties are chosen, they must clearly be encouraged to grow as fast as possible in order to provide adequate protection when the newly planted vines come of age. In order to avoid a measure of capital expenditure, some growers acquire cuttings and insert them liberally on the perimeter of their vineyard; if they take, and some of them do very easily, they should make a protective screen in a very few years.

It is also possible to obtain windbreaks made of plastic, which can be erected immediately, providing instant shelter from the wind. One such example is Paraweb manufactured by ICI, which can be attached to a series of vertical posts in whatever position it is likely to be most effective. Some English vineyards have already invested in a number of these screens which have been placed at intervals between the rows.

For advice on the most suitable trees to plant, it is worth approaching the Long Ashton Research Station, University of Bristol, Long Ashton, Bristol BS18 9AF (Tel. Long Ashton (027 580) 2181). The institute, which is much concerned with the production of fruit, has made a careful study of the damage caused by wind and the best way to provide effective protection.

Natural Windbreaks

A column of deciduous or non-deciduous trees planted in a position most likely to provide adequate protection to a vineyard could be termed a natural windbreak. Whatever trees are chosen they should be cheap to install and easy to maintain.

It has been firmly established that no windbreak should be too dense; the force of the wind should be diluted rather than diverted if the best results are to be obtained. Ideally the trees should be able to reduce the speed by 50 per cent and extend their protection over the largest area possible. It is also important to decide whether to plant evergreens, which are slower to mature, or deciduous trees which are fully effective only during the growing season. The first choice includes the Leyland Cypress, Lawson's Cypress and Western Red Cedar; the second is usually confined to poplars, willows and alders. It is also common to plant poplars and alders alternately.

Planting distances vary according to the species but as a rule the trees are spaced about 6 feet apart. Certain varieties can be planted more closely together, particularly when it is necessary to establish adequate protection at the earliest possible moment. Deciduous trees are more often planted as natural windbreaks; they grow faster than evergreens and are less affected by severe winters. Their open texture tends to reduce the force of the wind without causing turbulence, whereas conifers are inclined to provide too much foliage.

Leyland Cypress (× *Cupressocyparis Leylandii*) is one of the faster-growing evergreens, very disease resistant but rather too dense for maximum efficiency. They can be planted 6–8 feet apart and should be staked until they are properly established.

Lawson's Cypress (*Chamaecyparis Lawsoniana*) grows fairly quickly but also needs staking when newly planted. They can be spaced at 3 feet 6 inches to 6 feet 6 inches apart and may work out cheaper than *Leylandii*.

Western Red Cedar (*Thuja plicata*) is in many ways similar to Lawson's Cypress and may be planted at the same intervals.

A few pine varieties can also be used, although they are likely to develop more slowly. The Corsican Pine (*Pinus nigra maritima*) and the Austrian Pine (*Pinus nigra austriaca*) are often planted for this purpose. In damp conditions the Sitka Spruce (*Picea sitchensis*) is usually preferred and should be spaced a little further apart than the pines.

Of the deciduous trees, alders are probably the best bet. They have the advantage of being frugal in demand and can therefore be planted within the vineyard as well as on the perimeter. They grow well on a variety of soils and reach a manageable height.

The Grey Alder (*Alnus incana*) is generally considered to be one of the best, although it may turn out to be a bit more expensive than the others.

The Common Black Alder (*Alnus glutinosa*) is certainly cheaper and is eminently suitable for the heavy clays that seem to be a common feature of so many English vineyards.

The Italian Alder (*Alnus cordata*) may cost a little more but could well be the best buy. It is vigorous and able to maintain its foliage until the harvest. Alders are usually planted about 5 feet apart.

Birch (*Betula alba*) is quite suitable as a windbreak and can be grown fairly close to vines without causing distress. The trees should be spaced at intervals of 5 feet.

Poplar (*Populus Tacamahaca* × *tricholcarpa*) is vigorous and disease resistant. Clone 32 is the one usually recommended. It tends to burst into leaf rather early and is therefore useful as a protective screen against the cold winds of spring. They should be given a little more room, say 6 feet between each plant, and are capable of growing to a substantial height.

Other poplars include *berolinensis*, *gelrica*, *eugenii* and *rolusta*, the last of which is often chosen on account of its early bud burst; none of the poplars, however, can be planted too close to the vines and are best reserved for the perimeter.

Willow (*Salix alba*) can be closer and has other advantages to offer. It is not so greedy and is less likely to suffer from the various diseases that attack poplars. It roots very easily from cuttings, grows fast and can be planted 3 feet apart, thus providing greater protection.

One of the best is our indigenous Cricket Bat Willow (*Salix alba coerulea*) which makes an excellent perimeter windbreak; others equally suitable are 'Drakenburg', 'Liempde', and 'Vries', all varieties of *Salix alba*. It is also worth recommending *Salix aquatica gigantea* and *Salix* × Bowles Hybrid, both of which grow to a height of 25 feet in a few years. Unrooted cuttings of all willows can be inserted at intervals of 12–18 inches and thinned where necessary.

Windbreaks should be looked after during the first two or three years. Herbicides may be used to keep them free of weeds and the hose must be applied in drought conditions. Some growers favour the use of black polythene which should effectively cope with such problems.

Once established a windbreak needs to be trimmed, especially where unrestricted growth would compete with the vines and reduce the light and air. This applies particularly to those planted within the vineyard. Machines exist which can trim windbreaks up to a height of 30 feet and there are firms that undertake this kind of work for fruit farmers.

Artificial Windbreaks

The value of windbreaks for horticultural purposes is clearly demonstrated by the number of artificial substitutes available on the market. These are usually sold in rolls or bales at prices which vary according to the durability of the material and the height when erected. Most of the windbreaks are made from black or green ultra-violet-stabilized polythene, polyethylene or polypropylene with a porosity of around 50 per cent.

A popular make is 'Paraweb 50' which consists of 2-inch wide black strips spaced horizontally at 2-inch intervals with vertical bands at 39 inches apart. It is sold in widths ranging from 3 feet 3 inches to 7 feet 2 inches.

To obtain details of other artificial windbreaks, the materials used and the current prices charged, growers should contact producers at the addresses given in the Appendix.

Whatever the final choice may be, some care should be taken to see that the windbreak is properly erected. Special instructions for securing Paraweb can be obtained from the makers but for the netting type of barrier the procedure is more or less as follows.

The supporting posts must have a diameter of 4 inches and should be placed about 10 feet apart. A suitable length would be 8 feet of which 2 feet would be buried in the ground. Anchorage can be provided by guy ropes attached to stakes driven into the earth or embedded in concrete.

The netting is supported by two horizontal wires attached to the posts at the appropriate distance apart. It is usual to fold the edge of the netting over the wires and secure it in position by threading polypropylene twine through as a fastening. Galvanized wire of 9 or 10 gauge should be strong enough.

Frost

Vineyards can suffer frost damage during the winter, at the time of bud burst in the spring or just before the harvest in the month of October.

The vine, like the potato and the dahlia, is a plant that cannot tolerate frost during its period of growth. Swelling buds, green shoots and grapes can all suffer when the thermometer drops below freezing point. Matured wood, on the other hand, is able to resist a temperature of $-20\,°C$ ($-4\,°F$). The United Kingdom, with its maritime climate, is less vulnerable than other parts of Europe; cool summers are accompanied by relatively warm winters, and if the weather proves harsh, it is likely to be harsher on the Continent.

Damage caused by winter frost depends partly on the condition of the wood; some varieties ripen their canes better than others and are therefore more able to cope with severe weather. Provided the wood is sufficiently dry, reserves of carbohydrate will prevent the plant cells from freezing, and serious damage may thus be avoided. A sudden drop in temperature following a spell of mild weather is dangerous and likely to cause widespread devastation. Exceptional frost can penetrate the ground and kill the roots; light, sandy soils are especially vulnerable in this respect. The European Vine (*Vitis vinifera*), for example, cannot tolerate the sort of winters that they get in the Niagara district on the Canadian border. As a consequence, areas such as these are obliged to rely on American varieties and hybrids for their wine production.

English vineyards, fortunately, are unlikely to suffer extremes of this nature, although in parts of Europe frosts of unusual severity can sometimes occur, causing considerable damage. It is therefore quite common to see vines protected during the winter by a ridge of soil heaped up over the roots.

Fruiting buds are more vulnerable and, if affected, will remain dormant in the spring; care should therefore be taken when choosing scion wood for grafting. It should be possible to ascertain the amount of damage by slicing a few buds vertically with a sharp knife or razor blade.

Frosts that provoke the most anxiety are possibly those which occur during the first half of May. If the temperature should fall below −2 °C (28.5 °F) substantial losses will be incurred. In the United Kingdom spring frosts can also be dangerous if they occur in April, before the buds have burst into leaf, and gardeners will confirm that the risk will continue until the end of May. Thanks to our maritime climate, however, the likelihood of severe damage can often be less than that anticipated on the Continent. Much will depend on the site of a vineyard, and those which have been planted in vulnerable areas must expect to suffer accordingly. Sloping ground, from which cold air has plenty of opportunity to drain away without impediment, will fare better than the proverbial frost pocket, usually to be found in a valley or depression.

In the autumn early ground frosts are unlikely to cause any serious damage to the vineyard. In southern England the first air frost is often delayed until the middle of November, and this is just as well if the vines have been unable to flower during the first half of July. It is generally considered necessary to allow 100 days from flowering to harvest; although an air frost does not always ruin the fruit, it kills the leaves and destroys the unripened wood. If the grapes are unripe, this can affect the flavour of the wine that is produced, so the later the advent of an air frost, the better the prospects on all accounts. A temperature of −4 °C (25 °F) is sufficient to freeze the fruit and impart a disagreeable taste to the wine.

Not a great deal can be done to reduce frost damage without spending money. Good drainage and proper weed control will help; a system of training that is not too close to the ground and the choice of a site which enables any cold air to roll away down a slope must surely lessen the risk and may make the little bit of difference required to avoid disaster. In parts of Switzerland umbrellas are ingeniously fashioned out of straw and used to protect the vines from spring frost. Something of the sort could be undertaken with plastic hoods, but the cost of providing these would be excessive. Helicopters have been used in France to cause turbulence and disperse concentrations of cold air accumulating over a vineyard when a frost is expected.

For those who decide to adopt some measure of protection, there are three practical alternatives. The damage caused by a spring frost can be avoided or reduced by the production of smoke, by the introduction of warmth or by overhead irrigation. The do-it-yourself creation of a smoke cloud is likely to be the cheapest solution, provided it can be maintained over the entire vineyard; this will be possible only in the absence of wind.

Metal drums, suitably punctured on all sides, can be made to serve as incinerators. These should be placed at strategic intervals throughout the vineyard and charged with appropriate material for burning. The choice of what can be used will be a matter for experiment, so it is wise to stage a few dress rehearsals. Sawdust soaked in sump oil, peat, wet straw and green weeds, old motor tyres or tarred debris should make excellent material for the creation of an artificial smoke screen, capable of withstanding frost of −3 °C (27 °F).

Far more reliable but infinitely more costly will be the maintenance of warmth by means of an adequate number of heating devices. Special oil stoves are sometimes chosen for this purpose, but the capital outlay involved tends to discourage their use. European vineyards likely to suffer from the frost often install an irrigation system capable of providing water during the summer season, which can also be used for spraying the vines when frosty conditions prevail. The latent heat of ice forming on the fruit buds helps to protect them from serious damage.

2

Manuring a Vineyard

For those who are hoping to cultivate vines for profit in the United Kingdom, the yield of fruit per acre is one of the first considerations. Labour costs are of equal importance, but growers are unlikely to be satisfied with harvests which are below average. Vines which habitually yield insignificant quantities may or may not produce better-quality wines, but for the owner of an English vineyard it is the size of the harvest that pays the bills. It is easy to blame the climate for disappointing results which could be the consequence of bad husbandry. Failure is not always due to spring frosts or the incidence of coulure at flowering time; one of the causes could be a lack of soil fertility.

Before deciding how a vineyard should be manured, it is important to examine the soil structure. Although the vine is prepared to tolerate both light and heavy ground, it prefers a warm, friable soil, loose in texture and well aerated. Anything of a binding nature, whether it be of sand or clay, is quite unsuitable. For this reason light, gravelly or slaty soils are generally more acceptable than those which are more or less composed of clay and do not admit the air or allow water readily to run away.

Every textbook on viticulture stresses this; it is therefore abundantly clear that growers should improve their land if they wish to grow vines with any hope of success. It has not so far been understood that the successful production of grapes is a difficult undertaking, especially in Britain, where climatic conditions are hostile.

The best way to improve the texture of the soil is by frequent applications of humus. These can be of tremendous importance, either for the purpose of lightening a heavy soil or to provide some retention of moisture on a light soil, which would be the first to suffer from drought conditions. In addition, humus increases the earthworm population and stimulates the active growth of micro-organisms.

The late Professor Dr Lenz Moser, in his book *Weinbau einmal anders*, dwells on this at some length and advocates the use of green manuring to provide the appropriate amount of humus at a minimum cost. Such measures have become necessary in many parts of Europe due to the declining quantities of farmyard manure.

It is not enough to rely on one application of humus, hoping that it will last for ever. Vines demand a regular supply, enabling them to make the best use of the artificial fertilizers that are essential to a balanced manuring programme. For this reason the Lenz Moser vineyards are provided each year with a sufficient quantity of appropriate plants capable of creating humus during their period of decay.

For those who have access to farmyard manure, the provision of humus presents no problem. A regular application of 16 tons per acre every three years will furnish the vines with all they are likely to need, provided such dressings are supplemented with the correct amount of artificial fertilizers during the interim. If, however, animal manure is hard to get or considered too laborious to apply, the equivalent quantity of humus should be supplied in some other way. On no account, let it be said, should this valuable addition be omitted, for humus forms a vital part of vine husbandry.

Alternative sources of this active constituent are green manure, straw, compost, peat, sewage sludge and vine prunings.

Farmyard Manure

For centuries the fertility of European vineyards was dependent on the availability of farmyard manure. That was before the invention of chemical fertilizers, when the horse had not yet been replaced by the tractor. The English vine grower, fortunately, is not obliged to go far without finding a farmer with an adequate surplus of manure. Provided the muck-spreading can be undertaken without difficulty, his humus problem is solved.

Light soil will require 24 tons to the acre, but on heavy ground an application of 16 tons ought to be sufficient. The manure should be broadcast evenly all over the vineyard, if possible soon after the harvest; it can with advantage be lightly worked into the soil.

Farmyard manure should be applied every third year, with a supplement of artificial fertilizers during the intervening period. Growers must understand that organic manure is valued principally for its humus content and not for its mineral nutrients. Some European vineyards are now achieving yields far in excess of what was thought adequate fifty or sixty years ago. It has been estimated that the increase is due mainly to the use of chemical fertilizers. A ton of farmyard manure should contain approximately 9–11 lb of nitrogen (N), $4\frac{1}{2}$–$5\frac{1}{2}$ lb of phosphorus (P_2O_5), 11–14 lb of potassium (K_2O) and $12\frac{1}{2}$ lb of calcium (CaO). Some growers in fact add a supplementary dressing of 4–6 cwt of an all-purpose fertilizer to every acre of dung distributed.

Much will depend, however, on the quality of the manure available and the material with which the droppings have been mixed. Pig and cattle dung, for example, take longer to rot and do not act as fast as horse manure. The storage and stacking of the heap are also of importance if the valuable minerals are not to be wasted. As a reliable source of humus, however, farmyard manure displays its true significance and most valuable contribution to the welfare of a vineyard.

Green Manure

So many advantages favour the use of green manure as the cheapest and easiest way of providing humus for the vineyard. Plants used for green manuring take up nutrients from the soil which they afterwards make available for the vine, not only in the surface area but also at the depth where their roots decompose. This is of particular value in the case of phosphoric acid, which is not easily distributed in the subsoil. The roots also tend to break up in the ground, enabling water and air to penetrate more effectively. In addition, the labour involved in green manuring is not arduous and can largely be undertaken mechanically.

By adopting such methods for the provision of humus, the soil structure will be immensely improved; the fertility of the vineyard will be enhanced; and the dangers normally associated with monoculture will be substantially reduced. Any lack of moisture caused by vegetation in the vineyard is unlikely to be a problem during an average English summer. Green manuring should provide further benefits by reducing chlorosis, preventing stem atrophy and promoting the production of ripened wood.

It is important to remember that the plants chosen for green manuring will need the addition of minerals in the form of artificial fertilizers. These will be stored and distributed in the soil, so they will ultimately be absorbed by the vines. It is customary to choose plants that are not only fast-growing but also deep-rooted, and in this way the minerals are able to reach the levels in which the roots of the vine are obtaining their nourishment.

The seed must be sown each year in every alternate row, changing over in the following season. Obviously, this method of manuring is easier to operate where a vineyard is laid out with wide spacing, such as may be found with Geneva Double Curtain or Lenz Moser High Culture; it is difficult, although not impossible, where orthodox training methods are used. A gap of 12 inches should separate the green plants from the vine rows; anything less than this may increase the incidence of fungous disease, particularly of botrytis, for the recommended time of sowing is during the months of July and August.

Various combinations of seed can be chosen; growers may decide to ring the changes from time to time. Here are a few suggestions:

Type of Plant	Weight of seed (lb) required per acre
Summer vetch/mustard	178/18
Sunflower/summer vetch	14/62
Mustard/summer vetch/field peas	5/62/62
Horse beans/summer vetch/peas	45/62/62
Summer vetch/peas/bitter blue lupins	45/45/45

The seed should be well mixed and sown in July or during the first half of August. About 1½ cwt of nitro chalk should be used as a top dressing to ensure that the plants grow vigorously. A supplementary list of plants, which could be substituted for those quoted above, is given below, with an approximate weight of seed required to cover an acre of ground.

Type of plant	Weight of seed required (lb)	Time of sowing
Non-leguminous		
Rape	18	July–August
Mustard	25	April–August
Rye	90–140	August–September
Sunflowers	27	July
Bitter lupins	175	April–July
Leguminous		
Summer vetch	105–135	April–July
Winter vetch	90–135	August
Beans	135	July–August
Field Peas	135	April–July

Non-leguminous plants will require to be given a little more nitrogen if a balanced diet is to be maintained.

Green manuring plants should be allowed to grow to a height of 20 inches, although some of them (sunflowers, for example) will grow higher before they are cut down or flattened, prior to being dug into the topsoil. They should not be allowed to flower and should never be buried before they have had ample time to wither. If they are immediately rotavated into the soil, they will undergo a lactic acid fermentation, which will cause the ground to go sour and do more harm than good. Air should be allowed to get at them for a week or two before the cultivator is allowed to dispose of their remains.

Some growers prefer to maintain a strip of grass between the rows of vines, and there are advantages in preserving such a path, provided it can be kept under control with a mowing machine. On clay soils, for example, it is more agreeable to walk on grass after a heavy shower of rain, and although it may increase the potential risk of a spring frost, it has much to commend it.

Cultivation, for example, will be unnecessary, and to some extent the risk of soil erosion will be reduced. The population of earthworms and other micro-organisms will be substantially increased, with a consequent improvement in the general soil structure. The surface of the vineyard is less likely to suffer from the passage of machines engaged in the necessary duties required throughout the growing season.

Although it is possible to allow a green strip to develop naturally, growers would be well advised to sow clover seed after the ground has been carefully prepared and adequately enriched with humus. About 15 lb of seed will be sufficient for an acre of vines, probably less, and this amount could consist of white clover exclusively or a mixture of the white and yellow varieties. After five years the carpet can be rotovated into the soil and the area sown again.

Straw

Straw is one of the best sources of humus and also one of the cheapest. Unlike farmyard manure it is relatively clean and easy to handle. It is usually applied in the autumn after the harvest and serves as a carpet during the winter when conditions are damp enough to assist the process of decomposition. As the vineyard dries out in the spring, it can be worked into the soil. Some growers favour its use in the summer to inhibit weeds but it cannot be fully recommended for this purpose owing to the risk of fire.

An acre of vines will need about 2 tons of straw for adequate coverage. It is however advisable to add about 250 lb of nitro chalk in the spring to compensate for the loss of nitrogen caused by the gradual conversion of straw into humus. Bacteria in the soil require a supply of nitrogen to carry out this process and as a consequence may create a deficiency that will have to be replaced.

Straw can also be used in larger quantities to create a more durable cover. Apart from checking weeds, the artificial carpet preserves moisture and avoids the necessity for cultivation. About 4 tons of straw per acre should be applied in the autumn with the appropriate quantity of nitro chalk in the spring. In addition the full complement of artificial fertilizers must be provided in the usual way. After five years the straw can be rotavated into the soil and the whole operation repeated. Drought conditions may create a fire risk.

The beneficial effects of straw can be combined with green manuring. To achieve the best result, seed should be sown in July and immediately covered with 1½–2 tons of straw. An acre of ground will require about 40 lb of lupin seeds, 60 lb of field peas and the same quantity of vetch. During the spring the emergent growth and straw mulch should be worked into the soil. A supplement of nitro chalk should not be necessary because field peas and summer vetch are leguminous plants which provide a supply of nitrogen to the soil.

Compost

The production of compost may occupy too much time to be considered worthwhile by the average farmer; this is a pity because evidence has shown that soil fertility can be much improved by applications of this commodity.

The main contribution, as far as the vineyard is concerned, is the provision of humus, and in this respect compost can be more beneficial than farmyard manure so long as it has been properly made from the right materials. Annual dressings of compost applied to a vineyard soil composed of clay are of some significance and can have a profound effect on the future performance of the vines planted there. This has been visibly demonstrated at the Kingston vineyard belonging to the Merrydown Wine Company, which was able to provide massive quantities of compost made from apple pomace, broiler-house litter and straw. Formerly a brickyard, this uncompromising site was gradually transformed into a vineyard well able to match the performance of others more favourably equipped by nature.

It has also been established that plants absorb minerals much more easily from compost than they are ever able to extract from artificial fertilizers. The same applies to farmyard manure and follows the theory that plants are selective in their feeding and are likely to transfer the results of their diet to the animals that feed on them. This is a natural cycle that is not difficult to accept.

There are plenty of composting systems available for the gardener, and various containers are marketed for small-time production. These, however, are unlikely to be much use for an acre or more of vines. Nevertheless, it should be possible to benefit by adapting the principle laid down by the Indore method, for example, at the same time endeavouring to produce large quantities of compost in the most efficient way.

Farmers, who have machinery at their disposal, should be able to cope with large quantities of waste material. At Merrydown the residues obtained from pressing apples became an ever-increasing problem, which demanded the installation of expensive machinery to turn it into a profitable advantage. The pomace was not completely dry, and it arrived at a time when the autumn rains were scheduled to start in earnest. This demanded some degree of shelter such as would be provided by a Dutch barn. Bales of straw were acquired from a neighbouring farmer, and litter from a local broiler house was used as an activator. The materials were built up in layers, and aeration was provided by a tractor fitted with a scoop, which turned the heap at frequent intervals. A soil thermometer recorded temperatures up to 71 °C (160 °F), and for a time the finished product, besides being spread on the vineyard, was disintegrated by a shredder and sold in bags under the descriptive title of Pompost.

The choice of composting material will depend very much on what becomes available but there should be plenty of organic waste on a farm. Straw is an excellent ingredient because it allows the free passage of air, without which the heap will fail to decompose and turn into a form of silo. As an activator animal droppings will serve; chemicals such as calcium cyanamide have even been used. Every now and then a layer of slaked lime can be added to keep the mixture sweet.

Any organic material can be incorporated—such as pea and bean haulm, the green tops of any vegetables, weeds, lawn mowings, fruit residues and, above all, the discarded foliage and prunings from the vineyard. Temperatures should reach 71 °C (160 °F) and should remain for about a week over the 40 °C (100 °F) mark, effectively killing all the weed seed buried in the heap. As soon as the temperature starts to drop, the outside should be scooped up and deposited in the middle of a new heap conveniently built alongside. The ingredients should be kept moist at all times but must not be allowed to lose heat by becoming too wet.

Peat

Applications of peat, although expensive, are an excellent way of providing valuable humus for the vineyard. It decomposes slowly and therefore has a much more lasting effect than compost or even farmyard manure. It loosens the soil, stores water and facilitates the passage of air round the roots of the vine.

Being totally devoid of nutrients, it must be combined with an all-purpose fertilizer or accompanied by an appropriate NPK application if it is to be used as a substitute for farmyard manure.

Peat is usually applied in the autumn, once every three years, when it can safely be ploughed into the ground. About eighty bales will be required for each acre in order to provide the correct amount of humus.

A useful compost can be made by mixing a bale of peat with 10 lb of nitro chalk, 15 lb of basic slag and 15 lb of potassium sulphate. Care must be taken to ensure that the ingredients are evenly distributed throughout the peat. Water should then be slowly added to the heap, making sure that it is fully absorbed; 60 or 70 gallons may be required for this purpose. The stack should then be covered and left for a month before turning. After allowing it another month to mature, the compost will be ready for use.

3

Mineral Fertilizers

All plants depend on certain conditions if they are to thrive. Nature is not always in a position to guarantee these conditions, so the good husbandman will have to do his best to provide them. If the soil structure, for example, is at fault, he will try to improve it; if the site is exposed, he will take steps to protect it; and if the ground lacks fertility, he will do well to supply the missing nutrients.

It is not always appreciated that growing plants extract a number of soluble salts from the soil as well as certain gases from the air. Should the supply of these be limited, the horticulturist is in a position to provide those mineral salts required by the plant for its growth and well-being.

The most important elements needed for maintaining healthy plant life are: boron, calcium, carbon, copper, hydrogen, iron, magnesium, manganese, molybdenum, nitrogen, oxygen, phosphorus, potassium, sulphur and zinc. Some of these are needed only in small quantities and are therefore known as trace elements, but scientists have established that all these nutrients are of value only if they are present in the right proportions. That means that any gross excess of one item may cause an imbalance, leading to a deficiency of another. It is therefore extremely important to understand the correct relationship between the various elements, as applied to each individual plant, before any attempt is made to alter the chemical composition of the soil.

Vines, like other plants, absorb from the air carbon, which is able to penetrate the leaves in the form of carbon dioxide. With the help of hydrogen and oxygen, carbohydrates are produced, consisting of starch, sugar and cellulose; this can be achieved only by assimilation or photosynthesis, which is dependent on sunshine and the existence of chlorophyll in the leaves of the plant. It follows therefore that the best results will be obtained by the presence of sufficient foliage, combined with prolonged exposure to sunlight. Such considerations are of less importance to the vineyards of southern Europe, where sunshine is abundant, but must be carefully heeded in our cold northern latitudes.

For the vine there are five important minerals which are available in the soil and are regularly absorbed by the roots. These are calcium (CaO), magnesium (MgO), nitrogen (N), phosphoric acid (P_2O_5) and potassium (K_2O). Relative to the size of the harvest, nutrients gradually disappear and have to be replaced; this can often be achieved by normal manuring of the crop. However, as a test of the adequacy of such manuring, it is worth submitting soil samples for analysis every three or four years in order to rectify any losses that might be revealed. Alternatively, it is possible to adopt a plan, based on a specific formula calculated to provide all the necessary replacements. Considerable research has been undertaken in wine-producing countries in order to arrive at such a formula. It is nevertheless important to realize that biologists do not always agree; results in one area may be at variance with those of another, simply because the geological conditions happen to be different. For that reason any sort of plan can be considered of value only as a rough guide. As a consequence, the grower must from time to time refer to the laboratory for leaf and soil analyses if he wishes to maintain a satisfactory soil fertility.

A typical example of such a formula, adapted from Continental recommendations, is as follows:

Nutrient replacements (lb per acre)

Yield of fruit (tons per acre)		Clay soil	Loam soil	Sandy soil	Stony soil
Nitrogen (N)	2	45–55	55–68	68–84	84–116
	3	70–83	83–101	101–29	129–76
	4	94–111	111–34	134–74	174–236
	5	101–29	129–45	145–86	186–255
	6	113–38	138–62	162–207	207–84
	7	125–47	147–78	178–227	227–312
	8	130–55	155–90	190–238	238–328

Nutrient replacements (lb per acre)

Yield of fruit (tons per acre)		Clay soil	Loam soil	Sandy soil	Stony soil
Potassium (K_2O)	2	62–8	68–74	74–87	87–100
	3	96–106	106–17	117–35	135–57
	4	129–43	143–60	160–83	183–214
	5	142–54	154–74	174–203	203–35
	6	160–75	175–99	199–226	226–65
	7	178–96	196–223	223–49	249–94
	8	190–211	211–38	238–72	272–320

Suitable for all types of soil

		Phosphate status of soil	
		High	Low
Phosphoric Acid (P_2O_5)	2	29	42
	3	44	66
	4	58	89
	5	65	97
	6	73	111
	7	80	125
	8	86	134

These figures relate to pure nitrogen, pure potassium and pure phosphoric acid. To calculate the correct amount of fertilizer needed, the percentage of minerals present must be taken into account. In the case of potassium sulphate for example, which contains about 50 per cent of potassium, the weights given in the above table must be doubled when estimating the quantity required.

In Britain it is usual to give fertilizer recommendations in units per acre. These can be interpreted as lb per acre divided by 1.12, or as kilograms per hectare divided by 0.8. This is a convenience measure, for the number of units in a 1 cwt bag of fertilizer is equal to the percentage composition shown on the bag. To give an example: a fertilizer said to contain 21 per cent of N means that 1 cwt of the preparation contains twenty-one units of nitrogen.

It is also important to remember that a balanced mixture of nutrients applied to the surface of the soil may not reach the roots in the same state. Phosphates, for example, tend to remain locked in the topsoil, and potassium finds difficulty in penetrating clay. Nitrogen, on the other hand, is so freely circulated that it often gets washed away, particularly if the vineyard is on a slope. This is why phosphoric acid and potassium should be applied before the vines are planted, so they can be ploughed to a depth most likely to benefit the roots. By the same token, nitrogen fertilizers are often divided into separate applications, two-thirds being made available in the spring and one-third after flowering.

It is always difficult to recommend an appropriate manuring plan; so much will depend on the soil structure and results of analyses. It would be most unwise to rely entirely on a rule-of-thumb formula; all one can do is to examine the advice given by European experts, who are in a position to make suggestions based on years of careful research and experience. A typical manuring plan spread over a period of three years is therefore given as a rough guide; the quantities relate to an acre and should be scattered broadcast:

First year   about 16 tons of well-rotted farmyard manure or a corresponding amount of good compost.

Second year   76–114 units per acre of P_2O_5
136–86 units per acre of K_2O
84–105 units per acre of N
25 units per acre of Mg

Third year   86–124 units per acre of P_2O_5
162–212 units per acre of K_2O
105–26 units per acre of N
25 units per acre of Mg

Fourth year   as during the first, and so on.

A fairly wide range of applications are given, and these are likely to represent the limits dictated by the nature of the soil, together with the abundance of the previous harvest. The figures may seem rather high and are probably based on yields that are not usually achieved in England. It must, however, be remembered that some of the nutrients could be lost or, for one reason or another, not be available to benefit the plant. With the help of soil and leaf analyses, the grower should be in a position to make the necessary adjustments.

Soils rely on clay and organic particles for their capacity to absorb nutrients and retain them against leaching by persistent rainfall. This is often referred to as the 'base exchange complex' and its capacity to absorb such bases as calcium, magnesium, potassium, ammonia and hydrogen as its 'base exchange capacity'. The content of base exchange material is higher in heavy clay soils than in those of a light sandy nature, and therefore very many more bases will be required to saturate the complex in heavy soils than in light ones.

The pH value of the soil must also be watched and, if unsuitable, should be corrected. It depends on the relative quantities of hydrogen and calcium ions in the exchange complex. The more it is saturated with calcium ions, the higher will be the pH. Because they have a lower content of base exchange material, sandy soils require less lime to raise the pH by a given amount than clay soils. Conversely, when lime is being leached from a vineyard, the same amount lost will have a greater effect upon the pH of a sandy site than upon one composed of clay. Sandy soils therefore derive more benefit from smaller dressings of lime, more frequently applied. The higher the pH value and the greater the degree of saturation with calcium ions, the more substantial will be the loss of lime when leaching occurs. The rate of loss, however, will decline as the pH falls.

Vines usually prefer slightly acid conditions, but the most favourable pH value can vary according to the nature of the site. Soils with a low pH tend to lose calcium and magnesium, while those which are too alkaline can fix phosphoric acid and such trace elements as boron, so that the plants cannot reach them. It is therefore helpful to select fertilizers which, through their components, help to maintain the correct acid/alkali ratio. The amount of lime to be applied therefore needs to be related to the type of fertilizer used. Sulphate of ammonia, for example, removes its own weight of chalk from the soil, and Nitram nearly as much.

Good husbandry, however, does not entirely depend on the correction of mineral deficiencies. Soil structure, improved by the addition of humus, comes first and must be assisted by appropriate methods of cultivation. All these adjustments can be made more easily and effectively before planting takes place; it is therefore wise to be patient and prepare the site properly in advance.

Calcium

That applications of lime are from time to time desirable, except perhaps on chalky soils, is a basic principle known to every gardener. Vines, which prefer a slightly acid soil, are no exception to the rule, and vineyards should be examined every three or four years in order to determine the pH value of the soil. The plants react unfavourably both to a deficiency of calcium and to a surplus, so the task of maintaining an acid/alkali ratio is too important to be overlooked.

Calcium encourages the root system and enables it to absorb the essential plant nutrients. It neutralizes acidity and helps to produce a friable soil structure. An acre of vines could remove up to $1\frac{1}{2}$ cwt of calcium oxide with each harvest, and twice as much can be washed out of the soil by the season's rain, so it is important to appreciate the need for replacement. Something like 12 cwt of quicklime per acre will therefore have to be applied every three or four years unless the vineyard is on limestone. Nevertheless, it is wise to consult a soil analyst for advice in this respect.

A surplus of calcium must also be avoided. An imbalance of this nature produces chlorosis, caused by the vine's inability to use iron, a nutrient essential for the production of chlorophyll; this leads to a gradual fading and loss of colour in the foliage. The chlorosis begins at the growing point, affecting the young leaves first, and in this respect differs from similar symptoms caused by manganese deficiency, in which chlorosis affects the older leaves first. The foliage starts to turn yellow or even white, and this discoloration gradually invades all the extension growth; if very severe, the entire plant may become chlorotic, causing some premature defoliation. At the same time the flowers fail to set (coulure) or, if they do set, further development is severely checked.

In such cases it is advisable to use fertilizers which are going to promote acidity. Sulphate of ammonia, for instance, should be used rather than nitrates, superphosphate instead of basic slag, and so on. For the provision of humus, compost or other alternative forms would be preferable to fresh farmyard manure.

On chalky soils advantage should be taken of rootstocks that are able to tolerate such conditions, and arrangements should be made to purchase stock grafted on the *berlandieri – riparia* or *vinifera* crossings, such as 41B, 161/49, SO4, Kober 5BB and 125AA. As a further insurance against chlorosis, a foliar feed containing iron may be used.

Iron deficiency chlorosis can be prevented or corrected by the use of chelates. In these compounds the iron is attached to complex organic molecules which protect it against precipitation within the plant before it reaches the sites where it is prepared to function. Chelates can be applied as foliar sprays or as soil applications. As many as five sprays applied fortnightly may be needed, but a single soil dressing could suffice for two or three years. For a soil application by far the most effective chelate is Sequestrene 138 Fe (Fe EDDHA), but for foliar sprays, when the chelate bypasses the soil, Sequestrene EDTA and others may be used. They are quite effective as sprays and are considerably cheaper than 138 Fe.

A deficiency of calcium also causes the foliage to fade. The leaf blades start to turn yellow, with brown patches appearing at the edges. The vine is unable to extract the valuable nutrients from the soil and, if the deficiency is severe, the plant will eventually wither and die.

Between 2 and 4 tons of ground limestone or chalk per acre, depending on the soil analysis, are likely to be required for the average site before planting takes place. The application should be made in two stages, the first to be ploughed in before applying a further dressing to correct the pH of the topsoil.

Instead of ground chalk, which is recommended in southern England, or ground limestone, growers may prefer ground magnesian limestone (Dolomite) which is extensively used in orchards and glasshouses. It is a natural mixture of calcium and magnesium carbonates, about 40 per cent of $MgCO_3$ (9 per cent Mg), and corrects acidity as well as providing a large amount of magnesium at the same time.

Nitrogen

Nitrogen, as every gardener knows, is the most important nutrient required for growth; it is of significance in the development of chlorophyll and albumen, ensuring a regular harvest of satisfactory proportions. In its natural state it can be produced by leguminous plants or by the decomposition of plant material; sooner or later, however, it will be necessary to add it in the form of an artificial fertilizer.

Nitrogen can be absorbed by the vine only in the form of nitrates and when applied as ammonium sulphate, must first be allowed a short period of conversion before it starts to take effect. The exact time of application is important too because nitrogen tends to go straight down and is very easily leached out of the topsoil, particularly after heavy rain. This is, of course, much more likely to happen in light soils; penetration is not quite as easy in heavy clay.

It follows therefore that the dressing should be applied at a moment when the vine is likely to make the best use of it. Undoubtedly, this must be during the period of spring growth when the plant needs to make a vigorous start. Many growers spread two-thirds of the total at the time of bud burst and add the rest immediately after flowering, with the idea of swelling the fruit. Great care must be taken, however, to avoid an overdose at the later stage, for this will tend to interfere with the process of ripening, which is essential if the wood is to withstand the frost of winter.

An excess of nitrogen is, in any case, something to be avoided. Some English vineyards are likely to be fertile enough and, if excessively stimulated, produce too much wood at the expense of fruit. For good performance and respectable yields, the fruiting canes should be of pencil thickness with reasonably short internodes. An overdose of nitrogen weakens the plant, making it vulnerable to fungous disease and the ravages of winter frosts.

Nitrogen deficiency is indicated by the presence of small leaves, which assume a yellowish colour. The stalks supporting them take on a reddish hue, and there is a general reduction of vigour. Wine made from undernourished vines are thin and lack bouquet.

Although nitrogen is present in the atmosphere, the vine is not able to absorb much of it in this form and relies instead on its roots being able to find nitrogen in the soil, where it must be made available in a soluble state. It can be provided organically by farmyard manure, compost or green manuring; alternatively, it can be applied as an artificial fertilizer, and here there is a choice between nitrates and ammonium salts. It is of importance to understand the significant differences between these two chemical compounds. Sodium nitrate (16 per cent N) and calcium nitrate (15.5 per cent N) are already in a form that can be readily absorbed by the vine and should therefore be used at a time when they can be of most benefit to the plant. Their application should coincide with bud burst, so they will be able to nourish the plants before being leached out of the soil and wasted. Being of an alkaline nature, they are suitable for use on acid soils.

Slower to act are the ammonium fertilizers, the reason being that vines are unable to accept ammonia until it has been turned into nitrates by soil bacteria. Ammonium sulphate (21 per cent N) is most often used and usually applied not only just before bud burst but also in smaller quantities just after flowering. The acid residue associated with its use makes this fertilizer more appropriate for chalky, alkaline vineyards. It is less likely to suffer loss by leaching and works faster in friable soils that favour the presence of bacteria.

Nitro-chalk (21 per cent N) is ammonium nitrate mixed with finely divided chalk to make it safe and less of a fire risk. Half the nitrogen is in nitrate form and immediately available; the other half is in the form of ammonia, and the conversion of ammonia to nitrate is appreciable in about ten days if the soil is warm and moist. It is generally regarded as a quick-acting fertilizer and is usually applied during the dormant period, on account of its corrosive action on the leaves if allowed to make contact. It is more damaging to the foliage than any other quick-acting nitrogenous fertilizer. It is dustier than Nitram, for instance, and therefore more likely to drift on to the leaves.

Urea (46 per cent N) is sometimes used as a foliar feed and, as such, is able to provide an immediate stimulus. This could be of particular value where recognition of a nitrogen deficiency has been delayed.

Phosphorus

Phosphoric acid (P_2O_5) is a nutrient of great significance in the vineyard, and care should be taken to ensure that it is present in sufficient quantities. It is a potent source of energy and has a profound effect on the production of flower trusses and therefore on the yield of fruit. It stimulates the micro-organic life of the soil and strengthens the roots of the vine. It helps the wood to ripen, thus enabling the plant to withstand the rigours of winter and, like potassium, encourages the process of assimilation.

A deficiency of phosphoric acid is indicated by the appearance of dirty brown patches at the border of the leaves. It is usually accompanied by a magnesium or calcium deficiency, featured as a yellow background. It can also be identified by the production of dark leaves caused by an excessive concentration of starch. Another symptom, often displayed by the leaves, is a tendency for the veins and stalks to turn red. The stalk, at the same time, is inclined to sag, as though it had difficulty in supporting the weight of the leaf.

A harvest yielding 3 tons of fruit per acre will require $\frac{1}{2}$ cwt of pure phosphoric acid as a replacement (3 cwt of 16 per cent of basic slag). The fertilizer should be applied to the vineyard during the autumn, immediately after the harvest and before any cultivation takes place. At least 25 milligrams of pure phosphoric acid per 100 grams of soil are needed in order to satisfy the cultural requirements of the vine. A soil analysis which yields a lower figure constitutes a deficiency. As a rough guide, the following suggestions may help:

	Milligrams of P_2O_5 in 100 grams of soil	Additions of pure phosphoric acid in lb per acre	Additions of basic slag (16%) super-phosphate (19%) in cwt per acre
Adjustment of phosphoric acid	20	90	$5\frac{1}{2}$
Annual replenishment	15–20	90–135	$5\frac{1}{2}$–8
Phosphoric acid deficiency	10–15	135–60	8–$9\frac{1}{2}$
Severe deficiency	5–10	160–215	$9\frac{1}{2}$–12
Very severe deficiency	less than 5	215–85	$12\frac{1}{2}$–$16\frac{1}{2}$

Basic slag should be used only on acid soils; where the pH value is above 7, it is preferable to apply superphosphate. Phosphoric acid takes a long time to penetrate the soil and for this reason an orderly adjustment of the soil nutrients should be undertaken before planting takes place. It should then be possible to distribute the fertilizers to a depth where they can most suitably nourish the roots of the vine.

Good-quality basic slag is difficult to obtain today, so it is important to check the percentage of phosphoric acid with the suppliers. It may be necessary to make adjustments to the quantities applied.

Potassium

Potassium is available in the form of an ion, an electrically charged particle that can exist only in aqueous solution. When potassium sulphate is dissolved in water, for example, it disassociates into two electrically charged particles, the potassium carrying a positive charge and the sulphate a negative one. These are known as ions—cation and anion. Fertilizers are usually said to contain potassium oxide (K_2O), not potassium (K), because it was originally expressed in this way and the description has remained ever since.

The mineral is of the utmost importance to the vine for the production of starch and sugar. Without adequate supplies, the harvest will produce a wine of indifferent quality, since the plant will find difficulty in performing its natural functions. The presence of potassium has been found to exercise a profound effect on the nature of the yield and especially on the assimilation of carbon by the leaves. For the unimpeded ripening of its fruit, the vine should never be starved of this nutrient after flowering has taken place; it is not only important for the harvest but also essential for the development of the following year's crop. A deficiency affects the swelling fruit buds, causing them to produce smaller bunches when they finally burst into leaf and start to flower.

Potassium can materially help the new canes to ripen and, as a consequence, enables the vine to resist the frosts of winter. It encourages the roots to develop and counteracts the effects of drought by reducing the amount of water required by the plant for survival. A vineyard adequately supplied with this important mineral should have a good record of health capable of withstanding disease. An excess of potassium in the soil will result in a magnesium deficiency.

A harvest of 3 tons per acre requires a replacement of 1 cwt of pure potassium oxide (2 cwt of potassium sulphate) on sandy soil or $\frac{3}{4}$ cwt (1$\frac{1}{2}$ cwt of potassium sulphate) on a clay soil. The fertilizer should be applied to a vineyard with heavy soil in the autumn, but on sand and gravel the application must be delayed until the spring. As a general rule vines need at least 50 milligrams per 100 grams of soil in order to maintain a healthy existence.

Deficiencies of potassium are not immediately apparent. The first indication is a reduced output and an inability to resist disease. If nothing is done to put the matter right, the lower leaves will begin to show signs of discoloration, which manifests itself as yellowish-brown patches appearing between the veins and especially on the margins, which eventually appear scorched. These patches subsequently wither and die as the season advances. Such symptoms are often mistaken for magnesium deficiency, but there are others which may help to identify the true nature of the disorder. These include curling of the leaves and browning at the edges, insufficient ripening of the fruit, irregular development of the grapes (millerandage) and a premature shedding of the foliage.

Magnesium

Magnesium is an essential ingredient of chlorophyll, the green matter that colours the foliage of plants. As the function of chlorophyll is to help to nourish the vine by absorbing carbon dioxide from the atmosphere and, together with sunshine, assist in the production of carbohydrates, the availability of magnesium is of paramount importance. It has a critical relationship with potassium; therefore a satisfactory balance must be maintained between these two minerals.

Magnesium deficiency is frequently to be observed on very acid soils and is often encouraged by excessive moisture; the symptoms are among the easiest to identify and begin in June with a discoloration of the foliage. The older leaves of the plant are first affected and start to turn yellow or red, as the case may be, between the principal veins. In spite of this, a narrow strip of green persists alongside the veins, thus presenting a pattern that is clearly recognizable. An acute form of magnesium deficiency manifests itself as dead spots on the leaves, which then die prematurely. As a result of the loss of chlorophyll, the vine loses its power of assimilation, causing interference with the yield and quality of the harvest.

A soil analysis for exchangeable magnesium should reveal the presence of 12–15 milligrams of magnesium per 100 grams of soil if the vineyard is considered to be well provided. Up to ½ cwt of magnesium per acre could be utilized by each harvest, depending on the size of the crop; a further quantity will be washed out of the soil by the rain, and so an annual replacement will be necessary in order to maintain the status quo. It has been estimated that about 15 lb per acre is lost in this way on heavy soils and perhaps twice that quantity on sand or silt.

As a consequence of these considerations European growers are sometimes advised to apply at least ½ ton of Kieserite per hectare annually until a soil analysis has established that no magnesium deficiency exists. This works out at 4 cwt per acre and may be rather more than necessary for English conditions; half that quantity should be sufficient, especially as a heavy dressing could cause some damage to the roots. Severe cases of magnesium deficiency call for special treatment involving the use of magnesium sulphate in the form of Epsom salts ($MgSO_4$-$7H_2O$), which should be sprayed on the foliage three or four times in the season as a 2 per cent solution. The chemical may be included with the ordinary spray material for fungous diseases and will help to prevent stem rot.

4

Grafting

The American Vine

The botanical species known as *Vitis* is usually divided into two subsidiary groups; *euvitis* and *muscadinia*. Many of them are natives of North America; some can be found in Japan and other parts of Asia; while the *Vitis vinifera*, from which the best wine is made, is generally referred to as the European vine.

The production of wine, however, is not confined exclusively to *vinifera* varieties. Attempts were made at growing the European vine in the New World without much success. It soon became apparent that the plant was unable to cope with the extremes of an American winter or found it difficult to resist diseases to which it was not accustomed. Any chance of survival in the face of such hazards was likely to be eliminated by an aphis known as *Phylloxera vastatrix*, an insect which subsequently found its way to Europe and brought havoc to an industry that had lasted two thousand years.

In America therefore it became necessary to rely on whatever native species were able to tolerate the bug. Some of them, like *V. labrusca* for instance, although not completely immune, had certain advantages. By crossing them with other varieties, even with *V. vinifera*, it was often possible to produce vines that would achieve some measure of success. Thus we have varieties like Concord, Catawba, Delaware, Niagara and Scuppernong, cultivated in many areas of the United States.

There was just one snag. *V. labrusca*, from which a number of hybrids have been derived, produces grapes with a distinctive aroma that has been identified as that of methyl anthranilate. Whatever the merits of this particular variety, and there are plenty, the so-called 'foxy' flavour with which it has come to be associated is not altogether acceptable to the European palate. As a consequence, American wines, apart from those produced in California, have never really found favour with consumers on this side of the Atlantic.

The invasion of Europe by the phylloxera aphis drew attention to the indigenous vines of the American continent which were phylloxera resistant. A rescue operation had to be staged in order to save the *V. vinifera* from total destruction. The solution to the problem lay in the practice of grafting the European vine on to an American rootstock, and the different species were carefully examined in order to discover which varieties were most suitable for the purpose. Some had to be discarded because they were difficult to propagate; others were reluctant to complete a reliable union with *vinifera* scions. It soon became apparent that the best results would be obtained by crossing two or more species that were known to be phylloxera resistant. These hybrids were derived from *V. berlandieri, V. riparia* and *V. rupestris;* also to a lesser extent from *V. aestivalis, V. cordifolia* and *V. monticola.*

The three principal species have different characteristics. *V. berlandieri,* which grows in the southern states of Arkansas and Texas on limestone, prefers warmth and is less able to cope with low temperatures in the winter. It makes good grafting material and is not vulnerable to the phylloxera scourge. Rootstocks derived from its hybrids are usually recommended for chalky soils, for which they have a degree of tolerance. *V. riparia* comes from the cooler parts of the United States, further north, and is therefore less likely to suffer from cold winters. As an early starter it can become a victim to spring frosts but has the ability to ensure an early harvest when used as a rootstock. It dislikes chalk and prefers land with a good measure of top soil. Highly resistant to phylloxera, *V. rupestris,* a native of the south-eastern part of the United States in the neighbourhood of the Mississippi valley, is at home on dry, sandy soils. Unlike *riparia,* it is not precocious, so the rootstocks derived from it do not promote an early harvest. Bud burst is later, so there will be less danger from spring frosts, but the ability to withstand low winter temperatures may be suspect.

The Choice of a Rootstock

English growers who are planning to lay out a vineyard must first of all decide whether to plant grafted vines or to take a chance with

rooted cuttings. The decision will not be easy because of the
difference in price, coupled with the difficulty of choosing the
right rootstock for a particular type of soil. A careful choice is
important because the future success of the vineyard will largely
depend on it.

Most English growers who prefer to plant grafted vines tend
to accept whichever rootstocks happen to be on offer at the
time. Impatience of this kind can be regretted later, when it
becomes clear that a mistake has necessitated expensive
replacements. Such mistakes can be avoided by shopping
around for vines with the right rootstock and notifying a
supplier at least twelve months before planting takes place. He
will then be in a position to prepare the plants with whatever
rootstock is required instead of taking a chance by attempting
to anticipate demand.

When choosing a rootstock there are certain considerations
that need to be taken into account, and growers should, if
possible, seek professional advice. It is important to remember
that the choice will depend on finding a satisfactory relationship
not only between the rootstock and the soil but also between the
rootstock and the scion. Suppliers of grafted vines are unlikely to
ignore the second consideration, but they cannot fully guarantee
the first without proper knowledge of the soil.

Selecting a rootstock for a particular vineyard does not depend
exclusively on the results of a soil analysis; climate and the
incidence of insect pests must also be taken into account. It may
be helpful to enumerate the most important aspects to be studied:
the tolerance of chalk in the soil, resistance to chlorosis, the
degree of humidity, resistance to phylloxera and nematodes, the
acceptance of drought conditions, vulnerability to fungous
diseases and the amount of vigour that the rootstock is able to
transmit to the scion.

It should be remembered that American rootstocks are not, as a
general rule, too happy with very damp conditions, so it is worth
considering a few like *riparia* Gloire or SO4 that are able to tolerate
a degree of humidity. A long period of drought, on the other
hand, is less likely to concern the English grower; rootstocks such
as 110R and 1447P are therefore more appropriate for the South of
France and other Mediterranean countries.

Some of the more popular rootstocks are listed in order of

diminishing tolerance to alkaline soils containing chalk. A note about each may serve as brief guidance for those who are able to make a choice.

41B Millardet de Grasset

41B is a cross between the *Vitis vinifera* Chasselas and the American *Vitis berlandieri*. It is one of the two rootstocks generally chosen for vineyards situated on chalky soils, being able to tolerate up to 40 per cent of active calcium. It is moderately vigorous and, given the right conditions, will ensure a good measure of fruitfulness and a generous yield. It is fairly resistant to drought but is unable to cope with humid conditions.

333 Ecole Nationale Supérieure Agronomique de Montpellier

333EM is the alternative rootstock for use in chalky vineyards. Like 41B, it can accept a soil in which up to 40 per cent active calcium is present, although it is perhaps less resistant to drought conditions. On the other hand, it is better able to thrive in humid areas and is superior in preventing chlorosis. It is another *vinifera–berlandieri* cross, this time with Cabernet Sauvignon.

1447 Paulsen

1447P was obtained by crossing *V. rupestris* and *V. berlandieri*; both American varieties. It tolerates soils containing at least 30 per cent of active calcium and is usually found in vineyards where very dry conditions prevail. Indeed, it is considered totally unsuitable where the microclimate is dominated by rainfall.

161–49 Couderc

161–49C, a cross between *V. riparia* and *V. berlandieri*, is also used for chalky areas; it will accept 25 per cent of active calcium but dislikes humid conditions. It prefers a fertile vineyard with a friable soil but has now been more or less discarded in favour of SO4.

420A Millardet de Grasset

420A (*V. riparia* × *V. berlandieri*) can tolerate soils containing 20 per cent of chalk, although otherwise rather limited. It does well on friable soils but will not stand up to conditions of drought, nor does it take kindly to clay. It has a tendency to delay the harvest and to reduce the specific gravity of the must by overproduction.

Teleki Selection Kober 5BB

5BB (*V. berlandieri* × *V. riparia*) is similar to 420A in its toleration of chalk and is widely used in Germany for colder, wetter soils largely composed of loam and clay. It is a vigorous rootstock that dislikes dry conditions but has shown itself capable, in normal circumstances, of supporting a generous yield of fruit. It prefers a friable, fertile soil but has a tendency to suffer from coulure in vineyards that have been too richly endowed with nutrients. Resistant to nematodes.

Teleki Selection Kober 125AA

125AA (*V. berlandieri* × *V. riparia*) is as vigorous as 5BB and often used in preference, having many of the same attributes. It is resistant to phylloxera and well adapted to grafting techniques.

Selection Oppenheim No. 4

SO4 (*V. berlandieri* × *V. riparia*) is not as vigorous as 5BB or 125AA but is equally tolerant of chalk. It can be used in soils containing up to 20 per cent of active calcium and prefers rich and moist soils to those which dry out too easily. Vines on this rootstock are likely to mature more quickly, ensuring an earlier harvest and riper wood. Its resistance to nematodes is similar to, and to phylloxera greater than, that of Kober 5BB.

Selection Teleki 5C

5C (*V. berlandieri* × *V. riparia*) is another rootstock frequently associated with 5BB, 125AA and SO4. It can be used on fertile soils which are considered to retain a degree of moisture. It is less vigorous than 5BB and 125AA and is able to tolerate up to 18 per cent of active calcium.

110 Richter

110R is a cross between *V. rupestris* and *V. berlandieri*; it is an important rootstock for the South of France, where it is able to thrive in extremely dry conditions. It can manage as much as 18 per cent of chalk in the soil and, although it is inclined to prolong the maturing period, ensures a good must weight and a satisfactory yield.

99 Richter

99R (*V. rupestris* × *V. berlandieri*) is another rootstock used in the Midi. Although its tolerance of chalk is about the same as that of 110R, it is not quite as capable of surviving a drought. It prefers a porous soil without too much clay and is strongly resistant to nematodes.

1103 Paulsen

1103P (*V. rupestris* × *V. berlandieri*) can be associated with 99R, with which it has much in common. It can tolerate about 18 per cent of calcium in soils similar to those which suit the Richter rootstocks but is able to accept rather more humidity and certainly a higher proportion of clay.

140 Ruggeri

140R (*V. rupestris* × *V. berlandieri*) is a rootstock which can accept a relatively high proportion of chalk (about 18 per cent) in the soil. It is quite vigorous and is very well able to put up with dry conditions. Like all such rootstocks, it is probably quite unsuitable for the United Kingdom, where the climate is dissimilar.

Rupestris du Lot

Du Lot (selection from *V. rupestris*) is a rootstock of extreme vigour, which in certain cases can promote coulure and delay the harvest. It is able to cope with 14 or 15 per cent of chalk and a certain measure of salinity in the soil but is not entirely suitable for cultivation where conditions could be really dry.

3309 Couderc

3309C is a cross between *V. riparia* and *V. rupestris*. It is a rootstock which does not take kindly to heavy and binding soils but will accept up to 11 per cent of chalk. It prefers moist, fertile ground which is porous and clearly does not thrive in very dry conditions. Soils containing more than a limited quantity of sodium chloride are also unsuitable.

1616 Couderc

1616C (*Solonis* × *V. riparia*) is the rootstock specially recommended for use in vineyards containing a high degree of salinity. Lacking in vigour, it nevertheless likes a certain measure of humidity and will tolerate about 10 per cent of active calcium.

44–53 Malegue

44–53M (144M × *riparia–rupestris*) is a rootstock of medium vigour which is supposed to resist drought. It can tolerate up to 10 per cent of chalk but frequently displays the symptoms of magnesium deficiency. Resistant to nematodes.

216–3 Castel

216–3CL is another rootstock suitable for use on salty soils. It is quite vigorous and will put up with some humidity but is not happy with chalk.

196–17 Castel

196–17CL is also unsuitable for use on chalk. It is frequently chosen as an ideal rootstock for sandy soils, being fairly resistant to dry conditions and reasonably vigorous.

Gresot 1

G1 is able to put up with a fair amount of humidity and is also selected for use on salty soils. It will not tolerate chalk and is also shy of drought conditions.

Riparia Gloire de Montpellier

Riparia Gloire is not a vigorous rootstock and is no use on soils which contain much calcium. It is, however, able to support humid conditions and can be planted on land which contains sodium chloride. As might be expected, it will not tolerate drought.

Grafted Vines or Rooted Cuttings

The freedom of choice that now exists in the United Kingdom between the cultivation of vines grown on their own roots and of European varieties grafted on to American rootstocks has created a latitude that is likely to cause confusion in the minds of those planning to establish a vineyard for the very first time.

First of all, it is important to explain that the aphis *Phylloxera vastatrix*, which has created havoc in so many wine-producing countries, is still a stranger to Britain. Although it has been identified in English hothouses on more than a dozen occasions, as well as being reported in a couple of vineyards, the bug has never managed to establish itself in the United Kingdom. To prevent it from so doing should be an important priority, but the destruction of grafted vines in an affected vineyard would be deeply resented if the government failed to pay adequate compensation.

In support of rooted cuttings it must be emphasized that plants can be produced from them easily and inexpensively. No special skill is required to obtain a relatively high take from the abundance of wood available from an established vineyard after pruning has been completed. Ripened wood, with three or four buds buried in sandy loam, should produce a well-rooted plant in one season. Satisfactory results can also be obtained from green cuttings by mist propagation in an even shorter time. Sturdy plants produced in this way can be bought at a price lower than that which growers are obliged to pay for grafted vines imported from the Continent. With phylloxera safely in exile and English vineyards widely distributed, there would seem to be no good reason to adopt the methods imposed on Continental growers by circumstances which have not so far plagued our island.

There is more to it than that, however. The French and German vignerons tell us that grafted vines are better performers. They grow more vigorously because the American rootstock can be specially chosen to suit a particular soil; in addition they are more prolific. It has been difficult to establish this claim from the results obtained so far in Britain, but we are told that many foreign growers would continue to favour grafted vines even if phylloxera were eliminated by an act of God. Foreign opinion—which, of course, may not be shared by the British, who are feeling their way—would argue that in the thirty-year life of a vineyard, higher capital investment would be more than compensated by consistently higher returns.

For the English grower there is an additional advantage. Clonal selection has now become an established practice on the Continent, and grafted vines of popular varieties are readily available from listed dealers. No similar effort seems to have been made with rooted cuttings, although it should be possible to adopt the same selective technique.

While it may be difficult to believe that phylloxera can be permanently excluded from the United Kingdom, it is reasonable to suppose that the aphis may be effectively contained once it has been identified and reported; such is the considered opinion of the authorities responsible for the health of our plant life. It is therefore up to the growers to make the final choice.

Vine Grafting

The grafting of European vines (*Vitis vinifera*) on to a variety of American rootstocks has become very big business. During the months of February, March and April millions of plants are produced in Europe by a process known as bench grafting; this is in reply to a demand from the vineyards of France, Italy and other wine-producing countries that require a constant supply of grafted material to replenish stocks. The EEC has in fact introduced legislation to control the marketing of such vines, and the production is governed by a series of precise regulations. The phylloxera scourge has in certain countries prompted the imposition of a complete ban on the planting of rooted cuttings; although England is at present immune from such restrictions, the day may come when the Ministry of Agriculture, Fisheries and Food finds itself obliged to adopt similar measures.

Bench grafting in the United Kingdom is not impossible but happens to be just that little bit more difficult than it is on the Continent. Thanks to the climate, the production of satisfactory American rootstocks is almost impossible without some sort of artificial protection. Even the Germans have been obliged to buy land in Italy in order to obtain the results they are seeking; American vines apparently require rather special conditions if they are to produce the vigorous growth that is necessary.

This is a pity because the rootstock is a vital part of the finished product and one over which the grafter should be able to exercise complete control. Unfortunately, this will not be the case because of the need to rely on imported material, so unless the English are prepared to acquire vineyards in southern France or Italy, they will be obliged to resort to glasshouses if they want the best results.

Clearly, then, the importance of finding a reliable supplier must be the first consideration. There should be no difficulty in contacting someone in France or Germany capable of providing an adequate range of rootstock material, and indeed, if necessary, scions which have been clone selected. Names and addresses of suppliers can be obtained from the English Vineyards Association.

If the rootstock has to be imported, there is no reason why the scions should not be readily available from a domestic vineyard. Growers who wish to extend their acreage will no doubt use their own material; those who might consider vine grafting as a commercial enterprise will no doubt plant a range of the most popular varieties for stock. Clone-selected scions, however, will have to be imported, until some attention can be given to this sort of refinement in the United Kingdom.

If scions are to be obtained from an English vineyard, great care must be taken to ensure that the material is sound. Some *vinifera* varieties fail to ripen their wood satisfactorily, especially after a season of inclement weather. Müller-Thurgau, for instance, is notorious in this respect, and canes of doubtful maturity should be discarded immediately. It is advisable to test the scion wood by splitting it open with a sharp knife; this can be done by dividing the bud and exposing it to view. Any frost damage or drying out of the tissues will then be revealed, and if this is done with a number of canes, the general health of the wood can be roughly determined. The bud should be green if it is healthy; any discoloration will render it useless. As a rule, each cane should be able to provide four or five satisfactory buds.

Scion wood should be harvested early in December, before any serious risk of frost damage occurs, and stored immediately under proper conditions. This will help to preserve the carbohydrate content and therefore give a much better chance of success. By keeping the ambient temperature close on freezing point, transpiration and the loss of moisture can be avoided, thus providing the graft with the level of carbohydrates it requires.

During storage, measures must be taken to combat botrytis, which will be ready to attack wood kept in damp conditions. A preparation known as Chinosol, which has been marketed specially for the purpose, must be obtained from Germany, where it is widely used as a disinfectant. The scion wood must be

soaked for a period of fourteen hours in a 0.5 per cent solution
before storage and for a similar length of time in a 0.3 per cent
solution immediately before grafting takes place. The chemical
has the property of sealing the wood and reducing the
carbohydrate loss.

For many years it was customary to store both the rootstock
and scion wood in clamps until grafting took place. The canes
were laid horizontally, with each end buried in moist sand. This
was found more satisfactory than keeping them vertical with only
one extremity covered and certainly preferable to burying them
completely. Now it is more usual to seal them in polythene bags
(after the Chinosol treatment) and to keep them at a temperature
of 1 °C (34 °F). Should it not be feasible to control the temperature,
the wood should be stored in cool, preferably dry rooms, which
can be ventilated and kept clean. Fungous diseases are apt to
develop in moist and warm conditions and for storage these
should be avoided at all costs.

It should be recognized from the outset that botrytis presents a
formidable hazard to the success of a grafting operation, and it is
during the period of winter storage that the disease can be most
dangerous. It must be remembered that the spores of botrytis are
active throughout the year—not only during the growing season
but also in the winter. The vigneron will no doubt be satisfied if
he can harvest a crop unaffected by this destructive disease, but
he should be aware of the persistent activity it can display under
favourable conditions. The progress made by the spores during
the vegetative period may culminate in the production of a
number of useless canes, which fail to ripen and display the tell-
tale scelerotia on a background of whitened wood. Clearly, such
canes will never be chosen to provide scion material, but even the
storage of healthy wood, if it is inadequately disinfected, could
lead to similar conditions. Rootstocks are not immune from such
attacks either; it is therefore imperative to treat all the wood in the
prescribed manner.

Preparation of the Wood

The rootstock canes must be cut into short lengths, each about 1
foot long. They must, however, be cut in such a way as to leave a
stump at the lower end measuring $\frac{1}{2}$ inch from the bud. The scion
wood must also be cut and here it will be necessary to leave a

stump of ½ inch above the bud and an internodal length of 2 inches below.

All buds growing on the rootstock must be removed with a sharp knife. The operation should be performed with some care to ensure that the entire bud, together with the reserve eyes, has been completely cut out; at the same time steps should be taken to avoid inflicting unnecessary wounds. After treatment the rootstocks must not be allowed to dry out and should be committed to storage or used as soon as possible.

Once they have been cut, scion wood and rootstocks destined for storage must be soaked for fifteen hours in a 0.5 per cent solution of Chinosol. During this period the temperature of the liquid should be prevented from dropping below 10 °C (50 °F). Immediately after treatment, the wood must be kept in sealed plastic bags in order to circumvent the danger of drying out by evaporation and thus causing a concentration of the chemical.

Storage for any length of time means an ambient temperature of 1 °C (34 °F). Where the scions and rootstocks have been imported, it is possible that some drying out has already taken place; in such cases it might be wise to soak the wood in water before giving the Chinosol treatment.

The Grafting Procedure

Two methods of joining the scion and rootstock seem to be in general use. Both involve cutting the wood in such a way as to ensure a stable union that will support a vigorous plant. The one is generally referred to as the 'English Copulation Cut' and can be very skilfully performed by hand; the other, known as the 'Omega Cut' can be done only by a machine. A machine has also been invented to undertake the manual job, but an experienced operator can often do it better.

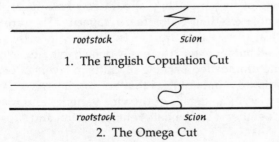

rootstock   scion

1. The English Copulation Cut

rootstock   scion

2. The Omega Cut

Special grafting knives can be obtained for the purpose, with one side of the blade level, so that a flat surface to the cut can be guaranteed. These should be kept permanently sharp for maximum efficiency. A slanting cut should be made both on the rootstock and the scion, taking care to ensure that they match in diameter. The cut should be made on the broad side of the cane which contains the bud or eye and in length must approximate to about one and a half times the diameter of the wood. In appearance the surface of the cut should be oval and, on the scion, fairly close to the bud. To ensure a successful graft the flat surfaces of the scion and rootstock should, when held together, fit each other perfectly. The second cut is made vertically through the exposed surface, using the blade of the knife in a carving action and twisting the knife slightly to form a 'tongue'. Both scion and rootstock are subjected to the same treatment, after which the two pieces of wood are wedged together in what should be perfect union.

As soon as the scion and rootstock have been joined together, it is usual, but not essential, to immerse the union in grafting wax. It is advisable to use wax specially prepared for the job and to maintain the recommended temperature when melted. Grafting wax is now available with fungicide added and by using it the risk of infection is reduced. It strengthens the union and helps to prevent it drying out.

After waxing the scion, it is customary to proceed with the next stage of the operation. This entails packing the grafts into boxes of damp peat and keeping them for three weeks in a temperature of 27 °C (80 °F). It is, however, usual to accumulate a number of boxes before turning on the heat, and if they have been packed in the approved manner, they should be able to survive in a stable condition.

The boxes can be made of wood, although plastic is now used in the interests of hygiene. They should be of manageable size, preferably not exceeding 4 cubic feet in capacity. They are usually made of deal planks that are not less than $\frac{3}{4}$ inch thick. They require no lid but must have an easily detachable side in order to facilitate the unimpeded packing of grafts in layers of peat. The boxes should be numbered, so that appropriate records can be kept, giving accurate details of the vine varieties and rootstocks included, together with the dates of completion and subsequent incubation.

The incubation room must have plenty of light and this will be important as soon as the buds begin to break. A greenhouse would be ideal, provided that temperature can be controlled. If it is allowed to fluctuate, the success of the operation will be seriously jeopardized. The heating must be evenly distributed; hot water pipes are therefore more suitable than a stove, which tends to overheat the immediate area without being able to reach the furthest point. Some kind of thermostatic control is essential, and various devices have already been made available for the horticultural industry.

As soon as the grafts have been prepared and waxed, they must be packed in damp peat up to a level just below the union. In order to achieve this, the box is laid on its side with the detachable side uppermost. By removing this it will be possible to arrange the grafts on a bed of moist peat in such a way as to allow the scion and grafted union to protrude beyond the packing material. The peat must have been soaked previously to an extent which would allow a handful to be squeezed without water actually running out. On the prepared bed of peat the grafts are then laid out not more than 2 inches apart, keeping the scions and unions more or less on the same level. When the row has been completed, a fresh layer of peat is added, covering the grafts entirely and providing an opportunity for the process to be repeated.

As soon as the container is full, the detachable side is put back into place, making it possible to restore it to its vertical position. The grafts will then be in upright, with the scions and unions showing above the peat. These must now be covered, and by far the best material to use is horticultural Perlite. Perlite is a natural mineral substance which has its origin in volcanic rock. For industrial and agricultural purposes it is usually refined and has the advantage of being sterile. It is therefore unlikely to encourage the development of botrytis and other fungous diseases. It has, furthermore, the advantage of admitting both light and air, thus promoting the formation of a healthy green shoot. The Perlite is brought up level with the top of the bud if the graft has been waxed; where no wax has been used, the Perlite should just cover the tip of the scion.

When the box has been fully packed after this fashion, it should be removed to a cool place where it can be kept until such time as the required number of similarly prepared containers are ready to be taken to the incubating room. Provided that the grafts have been packed and prepared in a suitable manner, there is no reason why they should suffer any disadvantage by being kept a week or two before being subjected to the heat. It must, however, be emphasized that much will depend on the moisture of the peat, and this will be a critical factor throughout the entire grafting operation.

When the required number of boxes have been completed, the whole lot must be transferred to the incubating room, where a temperature of 27 °C (80 °F) must be maintained for three weeks. During this time the scion and rootstock should be able to produce a gluey substance, known as the callus, which has the purpose of cementing the union and forming a living plant from the two pieces of wood that have been artificially joined together. Throughout the period of incubation a humid atmosphere must be permanently maintained; this can most effectively be guaranteed by frequently watering the alleyways.

As the shoots begin to appear, humid conditions must be allowed to prevail; more failures have been caused by drying out than are thought possible, and the boxes must be closely watched to see that this does not happen. As long as the grafts remain in the incubating room, they should be relatively free from botrytis infection, as the high temperature tends to inhibit the disease. After they come out, however, the new growth will be extremely vulnerable, especially when the thermometer registers 15–21 °C (60 °F–70 °F).

It will therefore be necessary to protect the young grafts during the hardening-off period, and for this purpose Chinosol can again be used. As there will be a danger of scorching, the concentration must not exceed 0.05 per cent, and some sort of 'wetter' (sulphonamide) should be used. Spraying ought to take place twice a week, at least until the grafts are removed from the boxes and planted out in a nursery bed. Rovral is an excellent alternative and may be used throughout the season; it is considered to be safer than Ronilan for young plants.

As soon as the grafts have become acclimatized to a natural ambient temperature, they can be planted in the nursery bed. Clearly, this should not be done too early in the year, although in England the climate cannot be relied upon. First of all, the boxes should be removed from the heat and placed in a cool room where some sort of protection from the weather can be guaranteed. After a few days in the cooler atmosphere, they can be unpacked and examined to ascertain how many have effectively formed a callus. Those which have been successful will be ready for the next stage.

Two alternative procedures exist for the final pattern of growth. To build up a sturdy, well-rooted plant must be the prime objective, and this will not be easy in the short season allowed by the British climate. In order to make the most of the season, the grafts must be planted in the nursery bed during the first half of May, before the spring frosts have finally disappeared. This means an effective method of protection from the weather (and that, of course, includes the cold winds) is essential. There are two ways of providing this. The traditional method consisted of earthing up the grafts (as for potatoes), so that the callus and scion were completely covered with soil. Some kind of provision could be made to protect the green shoots by heaping peat or sawdust over the exposed area. Alternatively, the grafts can again be waxed, this time creating a film not only over the scion and union but also over the young foliage. This coating will be sufficient to protect the vulnerable portion against the elements and eliminates the necessity for 'earthing up'. With this method, strips of black polythene are laid out on the nursery bed over a series of ridges or slight hummocks, the edges being secured by tucking them into the soil. The centre of the strip is then punctured with holes about 3 inches apart and the grafts inserted into the soil, so that they penetrate to a suitable depth. The nursery bed itself should be chosen with care. The soil should be friable and warm (clay is not really suitable) and the site well protected from the wind. In order to produce vigorous growth and plenty of roots, the importance of choosing fertile ground cannot be too strongly emphasized. Competition from weeds must be eliminated, and the plants should be under constant scrutiny for any trace of disease. Whichever method is adopted, the rows should be spaced at intervals of approximately 3 feet and the soil adequately watered when planting takes place. Those who favour earthing up must remember to level the soil round the grafts by the end of July in order to prevent the development of roots from the scion. No cuttings should be admitted to the nursery bed unless they have a complete callus ring.

At the end of the growing season, when the grafts have lost their foliage, they should be lifted and stored for future use. This can best be done in plastic bags, but before packing they should be washed free of soil and immersed for fifteen hours in a 0.1 per cent solution of Chinosol, at a minimum temperature of 10 °C (50 °F). While still damp they can be sealed in plastic bags and kept at a temperature not exceeding 4.5 °C (40 °F) until the spring. Grafts stored in this way can be kept in good condition for a further twelve months, but in such cases the temperature should not be allowed to exceed 1 °C (34 °F). Alternatively, the plants can be kept with their roots buried in damp peat.

Grafted Vines in Cartons

Raising grafts in cardboard cartons is an effective means of providing plants for immediate use. In this way a vineyard can be stocked with vines in the same year that the grafting operation takes place. Capital investment can therefore show an earlier return, thus reducing the overall financial commitment. By using the carton method it should be possible to market vines at all times of the year instead of only during the dormant period. Given the right conditions, grafts raised in cartons should develop vigorously and maintain a higher rate of yield.

The grafts themselves must be very carefully chosen. Only the strongest, with a fully developed callus, can be considered suitable, the remainder being consigned to the nursery bed. Vigorous top growth from the scion is acceptable, but any abundance of roots could be awkward and difficult to pack into the carton.

The cardboard cartons (Kartonagen) sold for this purpose are usually about 1½ inches in diameter and often as much as 9 or 10 inches long. The sides are perforated, and the grafts are virtually planted in these open-ended pots by using a specially prepared soil. This can be provided by mixing peat, compost, sand and garden loam in equal quantities or, more simply, by adding three parts of peat to one part of a good commercial potting soil. The object is, of course, to produce a friable, well-aerated mixture that will enable the roots to penetrate without difficulty. The carton is filled to a depth of 1½ inches before inserting the graft and is then topped up in the usual way.

To make a success of the operation it is almost essential to have a greenhouse with underground heating facilities. A plastic tunnel would, of course, be equally suitable, but some sort of protection is necessary in order to maintain an ambient temperature of 20 °C (68 °F) to begin with and certainly never below 15 °C (60 °F). It is possible to use a hot bed, but measures must be taken to ensure that a soil temperature of about 24 °C (75 °F) can be achieved.

The loaded cartons are stacked alongside each other in a box or confined area, so that they can be maintained in an upright position until they have taken root. As soon as they are assembled, they must be soaked with warm water and afterwards sprayed with a suitable fungicide to avoid botrytis. At this stage it is important to preserve plenty of humidity in the greenhouse; protection from sunlight is necessary only when it becomes excessive.

As soon as the roots start to develop (they can clearly be seen bursting out of the carton) preparations should be made to harden them off. Well-rooted grafts can then be transferred to an unheated house or frame, where they can be put into larger 4-inch pots, if required. Here they should spend at least a fortnight before being committed to the vineyard or nursery bed.

Chinosol

Chinosol W, as marketed by Hoechst, is a fungicide specially prepared to reduce or eliminate the development of *Botrytis cinerea* on the production of grafted vines. Basically it consists of 8-Hydroxy chinolin sulphate (67 per cent) + Potassium sulphate (30 per cent) and is available as a yellow powder readily soluble except in water of an extremely calcareous nature; in such cases rain water should be used instead.

A solution of recommended strength may be used three times as a general rule before being discarded. Special test papers can be obtained from which it is possible to determine whether the solution has lost its virtue, but in most cases these will hardly be necessary. The makers advise the use of plastic containers when soaking the rootstocks and scions but insist that the fungicide is harmless to mankind, animals and plants when diluted to the recommended strength. Instructions on the container suggest a twelve-hour soaking of the rootstocks and scions in a 0.5 per cent

Chinosol solution (500 grams to 100 litres of water) at a temperature not below 10 °C (50 °F). The same treatment may be given shortly before grafting takes place. Scion material can most easily be held in a netting bag and immersed in the solution for the approved period. Chinosol W is sold in plastic containers holding 1 kilogram of powder.

5

Vine Culture

Laying out a Vineyard

Methods of training vines for the production of fruit are numerous and tend to vary according to the different conditions that exist in various parts of the world and often in adjacent districts of the same country. The choice is usually determined after a period of time as a pattern begins to emerge that is dictated by the climate, the soil, the temperature and the available varieties. The development of a wine-growing district is also influenced by economic considerations which are likely to have some effect on the methods of cultivation. Variations of the Guyot system are therefore to be found in France and Germany, the Lenz Moser high-culture idea in Austria and the Geneva Double Curtain in the United States. Interspersed with these are the traditional methods that exist in the Champagne district, the Moselle valley and parts of Italy and Portugal, where it is customary to train vines overhead.

The first consideration therefore is to decide on a method of training. This may well be determined by the nature of the site, especially if the vineyard is to be on a steep slope. If the vines are to be supported on some kind of wire trellis, a choice of direction will have to be made. Traditionally the rows of vines should run north and south, so that each plant benefits from the maximum sunshine, but this may be inadvisable if the ground slopes steeply to the east or west. Generally speaking, it is better to follow the contours of the land, especially if cultivation is to be undertaken by a tractor.

Equally important is the depth of the headland. Machines must have sufficient space to turn, although some saving can be made by manoeuvring the tractor into every second row when cultivation or spraying is due to take place. It must be remembered that vineyards whose owners initially prefer to do without mechanization may subsequently be extended, necessitating the use of a tractor or some kind of spraying apparatus.

The method of training that is finally chosen will influence the distance between the rows, the distance in each row between the vines, the length of the stem or trunk and the height of the leaf canopy. It will also determine the number of fruiting buds carried by each plant.

The Distance between the Rows

In very favourable sites, such as are to be found in the Médoc, the Rheingau, the Côte-d'Or and the Moselle valley, there has always been a tendency to plant as many vines as possible to the hectare. The same applies in Champagne. This is understandable where the value of the fruit justifies the employment of manual labour. The rising cost of manpower, however, has meant that vineyards all over the world are relying on mechanized cultivation of the land, and growers are employing fewer and fewer people to look after their crops.

As a result, the rows of vines must be spaced wide enough apart to accommodate a tractor, especially if some kind of wire trellis is being used. The size of the alleyway will therefore be determined by the width of the tractor, which must be allowed to pass easily down the middle without damaging the foliage on either side. It is with this in mind that special vineyard tractors have been designed for use where spacing is narrow.

Not everyone, however, is prepared to invest in a vineyard tractor, which may or may not be suitable for other work. Farmers will certainly prefer to use their own machinery whenever they can, and if agricultural tractors have an average width of 5 or 6 feet, provision must be made to accommodate them. About 15 inches' clearance must be allowed for on either side, which means the addition of 2 feet 6 inches to the width of the tractor. So if the tractor is 5 feet wide, the rows of vines should not be closer than 7 feet 6 inches.

Vineyard tractors are about 3 feet wide and are able to operate with less clearance on each side. It should therefore be possible for the rows to be spaced at a distance of 5 feet or even less, making it possible to plant more than 2,000 vines to the acre.

Where vineyards have chosen to adopt the Lenz Moser or Geneva Double Curtain systems, the clearance needed on either side of the tractor will have to be greater in order not to damage the mass of foliage emerging from the trellis. It will therefore be necessary to add at least 5 feet to the width of the tractor to determine the correct distance between the rows.

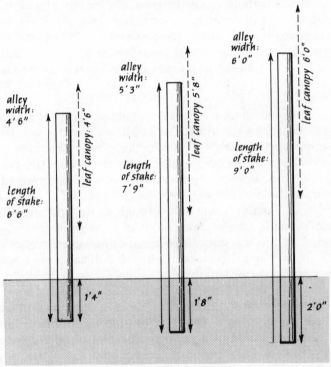

alley width: 4' 6"

length of stake: 6' 6"

leaf canopy: 4' 6"

1' 4"

alley width: 5' 3"

length of stake: 7' 9"

leaf canopy 5' 8"

1' 8"

alley width: 6' 0"

length of stake: 9' 0"

leaf canopy 6' 0"

2' 0"

3. Laying out a vineyard: examples of the recommended formulae

The Distance between the Vines

As might be expected, the spacing of vines along the rows will depend on the fertility of the vineyard, together with the vigour of the vine and its rootstock. In certain soils the growth is appreciably stronger; again the choice of a vigorous rootstock like Kober 5BB is likely to demand wider spacing. However desirable it may be to plant as many vines as will conveniently fit into an acre, it is very important to allow enough room for the foliage and to avoid excessive overcrowding. Experience has shown that a small gap should be apparent between the extremities of adjacent vines, and that overlapping should preferably be avoided, if the vines are to remain healthy and free from fungous diseases.

It can therefore be concluded that spacing between vines should not exceed 4 feet on poor soils and could be 6 inches less for rootstocks without reputed vigour. On the other hand, wider spacing is to be recommended for richer soils, especially when the vines are grafted on to strong rootstocks. In such cases the distance between vines could be as much as 6 feet 6 inches, although for the most part a limit of 5 feet should be adequate.

The Length of the Stem

As the vine becomes older, the stem gradually thickens into what could be described as a trunk. The length of this old wood, which plays an important part in the production of fruit, should be more or less related to the area available for the roots. The correct height for the stem or trunk can therefore be determined by measuring the distance between the trellises and dividing this figure by 3. Clearly, this is only a rough guide, and allowances should be made for the type of soil and the amount of vigour provided by the rootstock. The method, however, works very well with rows up to 7 feet apart; where this distance is exceeded, some reduction to the length of the stem will have to be made. We may conclude, then, that when the rows are planted 6 feet apart, the vines should be encouraged to develop a trunk measuring up to 2 feet. In poor soils the stem can be a few inches lower. Avenues with a width of more than 7 feet usually belong to systems like the Lenz Moser or Geneva Double Curtain, which have their own recommendations.

The Height of the Leaf Canopy

The size of the leaf canopy is of particular importance and plays a vital part in the quality of the fruit. A common error with the Guyot system of training is to restrict the height of the leaf surface to an inadequate size, thus curtailing the efficiency of the vine and reducing its full ripening potential. European growers maintain that a generous leaf canopy not only improves the quality of the fruit but also increases the yield and helps the wood to ripen.

It is important to understand this basic principle from the start, so that the posts supporting the trellis work are not too short, making it impossible to support a leaf surface of adequate dimensions. It has been more or less established that this wall of foliage should have a height equal to the width of the alleyway separating the rows of trellis. This means that for a 6-foot canopy it will be necessary to use stakes that are 9 feet long.

Clearly, such recommendations are not always possible to follow, and in certain cases the amount of foliage produced will be determined largely by the vigour of growth. It is of importance, however, to make provision for an adequate leaf area from the start.

Planting a Vineyard

Vines can be planted in the autumn or during the spring. Each period has advantages and disadvantages, and the grower must decide for himself which time to choose. Planting in the autumn can be effected without the addition of water and allows the vine plenty of time to settle in before the growing season starts. As against that, however, it will be obliged to survive the winter, which may be severe enough to destroy a young plant. In any case, it is wise to protect a grafted vine by heaping soil over the lower buds.

Whatever the pros and cons, growers for the most part choose the spring, and the best time to undertake this operation seems to be during the month of April, when the vine is just about ready to start growing. Left as late as this, the graft has little time to suffer the effects of a cold, dry spring, which could well be harmful unless certain precautions are taken.

Should the plants arrive prematurely from a supplier, they should be kept in a shady place out of doors, with their roots buried in the soil and the scions protected from the frost either by waxing or by covering with straw. Alternatively, they could be stored in a cellar or outhouse, again with their roots covered by a layer of moist sand.

Before planting, the roots should be trimmed to a length of 2 inches or less and the scion cut back to one or two buds. If possible, the bud between the scion and the previous year's shoot should be retained and encouraged to grow, because this should produce the most vertical shoot. The important roots are those which appear at the lowest extremity; those emanating from the scion or from any other part of the rootstock should be completely removed.

Some Continental growers immerse the scion and union in a special grafting wax in order to protect them from the weather. If this is not done, it will be necessary to cover the exposed portion with peat or sawdust until bud burst has taken place.

The vines must be soaked for an hour or two before planting, and some provision must be made for a supply of water, so that the plants can be 'puddled in'. It must be assumed that the grower has decided in advance what method of training will be adopted and therefore what spacing must be allowed between the plants and the rows. Some consideration must be given to the type of soil available, for this will determine the depth at which to plant. It must be remembered that vines prefer an aerated soil and cannot thrive if their roots are unable to breathe. Grafted vines usually have a rootstock at least 1 foot long, and if these are planted too deeply in heavy soils, they will try to develop roots near the surface and will waste considerable energy in doing so.

It is important to give a little thought to the layout of the vineyard. Rows are supposed to run from north to south, but such an arrangement must often be abandoned because of the physical contours of the site. It is also important at the outset to consider the shape of the vineyard and how it will effect the use of netting as a convenient protection against the menace of a predatory bird population.

When trimming the vines before planting, care should be taken to prepare no more than the quantity intended to be dealt with the same day. Roots are more likely to function properly if they have not been allowed to dry out.

Holes must be prepared, at the appropriate distances, that are approximately 1 foot in depth. Something like a pyramid of specially prepared soil, without manure or artificial fertilizers, should then be placed in the hole, over which the shortened roots of the vine can be assembled. The soil may be prepared in advance and should consist of loam and peat mixed in equal proportions. The roots can then be covered with some more of the mixture and watered before filling the hole and firming. Well-rotted compost may be used instead of peat, but farmyard manure and inorganic fertilizers must be avoided in case they should burn the roots.

Care must be taken with grafted vines to ensure that the union is at least 1½ inches above ground, and in heavy soils, of course, the union will have to be higher still. If the scion and graft have not been immersed in special grafting wax, it will be necessary to cover them with a mound of sawdust, peat moss or sand in order to prevent damage from drying winds. As soon as the buds have burst into leaf, the protective mound should be removed, together with any rootlets that may have been formed by the scion.

Grafted vines are sometimes sold in special sleeves known as 'Kartonagen'. These should be planted in the open vineyard at the end of June provided they have had sufficient time to harden off. Some care needs to be exercised when planting, to ensure that the protruding roots are undamaged. A subsequent period of drought will necessitate the appropriate application of water.

For the first year a vine must be encouraged to produce a straight, virile stem of some 6 or 7 feet; in order to do this, any side shoots must be rubbed off as soon as they appear. A bamboo cane fastened to a horizontal wire will be necessary to support the stem, which should be attached to it at frequent intervals in order to maintain vertical growth. A crooked trunk should be avoided at all costs.

If rabbits or hares cannot be kept out of the vineyard by wire netting on the perimeter, it will be necessary to protect the young vines with some kind of sleeve; these animals find the new vine shoots remarkably succulent.

As soon as planting has been completed, the vineyard should be rotavated in order to break up the soil compaction caused by the inevitable traffic of men and machines.

Vineyard Management in the First Two Years

As soon as bud burst occurs, the plants should be examined in order to determine what should be retained. Only one shoot must be allowed to grow; this will eventually become the permanent stem or trunk, planned to carry the fruiting canes in subsequent years. The most vigorous shoot is not always the best to choose; it is better to retain the one which lies close to the scion, as this is likely to prove most satisfactory when fully grown. As already stated, the stem should be encouraged to grow as vertically as possible, and every effort must be made to ensure this. Having decided what to preserve, all other growth should be removed at an early date.

As the young stem develops, it will need to be fastened to a bamboo stake at every 8 inches of growth. Any laterals that appear should be immediately rubbed out; tardy removal leaves a wound, which could have unfortunate consequences.

Attention should be paid to the potential threat of downy mildew, which is always a danger in young vineyards and nursery beds. Spraying should start at an early date, perhaps by the end of May, and the routine should continue until the beginning of September. Organic sprays must be used initially, but copper, in one of its forms, could be applied towards the end of the season. It is also desirable to control the weeds which, if allowed to flourish, will heighten the risk of peronospora.

As it is desirable to produce the main stem as soon as possible, whatever method of training is envisaged, the season's growth should not be too drastically pruned unless it has proved to be totally inadequate. Some growers adopt the policy of cutting down to two buds and starting all over again with the business of establishing a stem during the second growing season. The reason given for this treatment is that the plant will benefit by developing a stronger rooting system. It is debatable whether this argument is altogether sound.

To start with, the first harvest will be postponed for twelve months or possibly longer if a high-culture system has been adopted, and in the light of experience, future yields will be affected by such measures. It has been established that severe pruning is likely to stimulate excessive production of wood at the expense of fruit, particularly if a vigorous rootstock such as Kober 5BB or 125AA has been used. In certain cases the yield of fruit could be substantially reduced for a number of years as a result of coulure or simply by reason of excessive growth.

It can be accepted therefore that the season's growth should be cut back to two buds only if it has failed to reach a length of 12 inches. With anything less than 4 inches, the plant is likely to be faulty and should be replaced. Some growers meet this eventuality by potting up a few extra grafts in order to use them as substitutes.

For every foot of growth an extra bud can be retained, so it follows that three buds can be left on plants which have produced

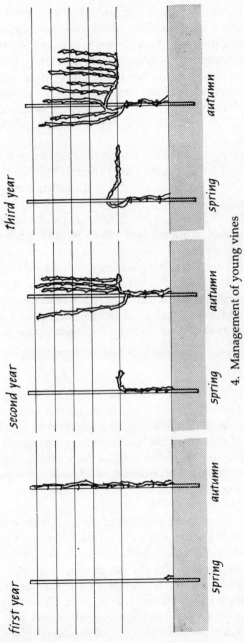

4. Management of young vines

more than 1 foot of stem, four buds up to 3 feet and so on. If the ground is fertile, another bud may be included. Six or seven buds can be left on a plant that has grown to a height of 5 feet, and this may be about right for a Guyot system of training. Ideally, the top of the stem should be 4 inches below the bottom wire, although much will depend on the length of the internodes and the ripeness of the wood. The height of the stem will be governed by the individual grower, who will decide which method of training he wishes to adopt.

During the second season the buds which have been retained will start to sprout unless they are controlled. Provided all is well, it will be possible to encourage the first fruiting canes in the hope that a limited harvest of fruit can be achieved in the following year. In order to do this, up to four buds can be left at the top of the stem, the rest being rubbed off when they reach the 'woolly' stage (March/April).

At this juncture it must be assumed that a wire trellis has been provided, so that the growing shoots can be tethered before they become damaged by the wind. Again, it will be necessary to be on guard against the dangers of fungous disease, and in particular against the threat of downy mildew, should the weather turn humid.

The Wire Trellis

The vine is a climbing plant. In order to produce an abundance of fruit, it must be restricted by pruning and trained to a shape that is easy to handle and likely to give a satisfactory yield. There are many ways of achieving this: perhaps the commonest are obliged to involve the use of some kind of wire trellis. In the United Kingdom, where the Guyot method of training is popular, it is worth examining the various recommendations before deciding how to set it up.

The trellis consists of a number of vertical posts and horizontal wires, erected in such a way as to form a framework to which the fruiting canes of the vine may be secured. The posts are usually made of wood, chestnut for choice, or oak; pine and larch are also used and the stakes are treated with a preservative frequently containing copper, arsenic and chromium. Growers can arrange to have their posts professionally impregnated with tar or can soak them for ten days in a solution of copper sulphate in order to lengthen their life. It is also possible to obtain metal posts specially designed for the job, but these must be imported from the Continent. About twenty years ago an Austrian firm produced the so-called Voest iron stakes, which are constructed in such a way as to be adaptable and therefore suited to all kinds of trellis work. Special treatment against rust guarantees a life of at least thirty years. Vineyard posts have also been made of cement or plastic, but these, together with the Voest type of metal stakes, must be imported, as they are unlikely to be manufactured in the United Kingdom. Whatever type is used, it will be necessary to erect them at intervals of 15–20 feet in order to provide a satisfactory framework for the wires. End posts, which bear a considerable strain if the wires are taut, need to be thicker and, when made of wood, should have a diameter of 5–6 inches.

The vines themselves will require individual supports, at least during the first few years of their lives. Bamboo stakes are often used initially but will have to be replaced by something more permanent until the plants have developed a sturdy trunk capable of supporting the abundant foliage produced by the fruiting canes. Short lengths of galvanized wire (gauge 8 or thereabouts), secured to the lowest part of the trellis, should be quite adequate for the purpose. As the vine becomes older, these supports can be discarded. Wire used on the trellis should be galvanized or covered with plastic to avoid rust; some growers use special plastic cord but this is liable to be severed by secateurs during the harvest. It is customary to use a thicker gauge for the lowest wire of the trellis and to employ some kind of straining device to keep it taut. These are adjustable and can be tightened when necessary. Growers who prefer to arch their fruiting canes will find it necessary to provide two such wires, one approximately 1 foot higher than the other, both fitted with a strainer. Above these, at predetermined heights, come the single or double wires used to contain the season's vegetative growth. Double wires are usually attached to short lengths of chain at their extremities, so that they can be raised further from the ground as the season advances. The end post should not be vertical but slanted at an angle of 60° to the ground, with the apex immediately above the point at which the anchoring wire enters the ground. The two wires connecting the end post to the anchor should be attached to each other approximately 6 inches below

5. The wire trellis:

(a) Five permanent
single wires

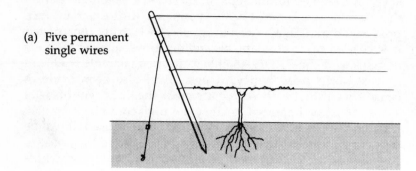

(b) Four single wires
and one
double wire

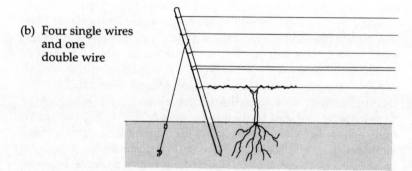

(c) Three single wires
and one movable
double wire

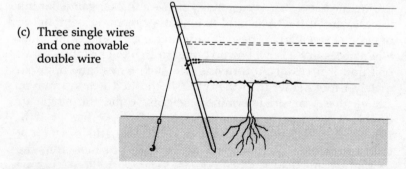

the surface of the soil, and the end post itself must be anchored by a wire of a gauge adequate to take the strain. It is better to treat the anchor as a separate unit, equipped with its own wire, to which an additional length from the end post can be attached.

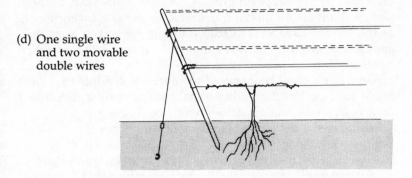

(d) One single wire
and two movable
double wires

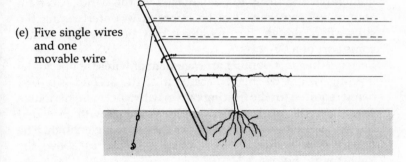

(e) Five single wires
and one
movable wire

Galvanized wire used to anchor the end posts and support the fruiting canes should be fairly stout, about 12 gauge, whereas those required to contain the season's growth could be less substantial.

Anchors can range from a sizeable rock, buried at the appropriate point, to a metal disk that can be screwed into the ground with a special detachable implement. An equally effective but rather more cumbersome method necessitates the provision of a hole filled with concrete, in which some kind of fastening device can be embedded.

There are several ways of erecting a wire trellis for vines and growers must decide which framework suits their own training system. Assuming that five separate levels are needed for the average Guyot system, a decision will have to be made as to whether single wires only are to be used or whether it will be advantageous to have a double detachable wire hooked on to each side of the supporting posts. Double wires such as these almost eliminate the labour required to tie in the growing shoots as the season advances; instead they can be tucked in as they appear and the pair of wires moved to a new position when necessary.

Some labour will be required to sever the tendrils that have made contact, but the saving of galvanized wire at its present price is a consideration that can hardly be ignored.

Wiring of the trellis can take the following forms:

1. Five single wires fixed permanently at strategic intervals. This method will necessitate a certain amount of labour, particularly in the early stages, when the new shoots are vulnerable and likely to be damaged by the wind. A certain amount of protection can be afforded by intertwining the subsequent growth but initially it may be necessary to use some sort of a tie-gun.

2. Perhaps the most popular arrangement of wires for horizontal training would be the replacement of the second (the first being required for the fruiting canes) with a permanent double wire. This will ensure security for the young growth, provided the shoots are tucked in as soon as they are long enough. The double wire should be positioned 8–12 inches above the lowest wire, not more.

3. Another way of obtaining the same result would be to do away with the third strand and allow the double wire to take its place as soon as the young growth justified the move. The two top wires remain in a permanent position, enabling the shoots to grasp hold of them with their tendrils.

4. Alternatively, it is possible to make do with one or two double wires only, which can be moved to fresh positions as occasion demands; growers may, however, encounter some problems with this system.

5. An ingenious compromise, which might appeal and should certainly be tried, consists in having a single movable strand that can be used successively in each position, thus converting one wire into two.

All these wiring systems are possible with Guyot pruning methods; whether the fruiting canes are horizontal or arched, occupying one wire of the trellis or requiring two in order to support the curve. Growers who favour the arched cane are usually obliged to use longer posts by way of guaranteeing an adequate leaf canopy.

Pruning Techniques

The first thing to understand about pruning is that vines bear fruit almost exclusively on growth made during the previous year. A bunch of grapes can occasionally be found on one of the water shoots sprouting from the older wood but this is a relatively rare occurrence. The most fruitful shoots are considered to be those that sprout from a 1-year-old cane which in turn has been developed from wood of the previous year.

The object of pruning a vine is to regulate the growth of a climbing plant that is accustomed, in its wild state, to make use of a tree or some similar support to maintain its upward growth. Cultivation, of which pruning forms an essential part, improves the quality of the fruit and provides the plant with the most favourable conditions under which it can thrive. The removal of unwanted foliage, allowing both light and air to penetrate the leaf canopy, substantially contributes to the health of the plant and averts the danger of fungous disease.

Growers should endeavour to find a balance between the number of buds they decide to leave on a vine and the size of the area occupied by the roots. Clearly, much will depend on the intensity of planting; generous spacing between the vines must surely guarantee a larger crop and therefore justify a longer fruiting cane. In Germany they have a formula that deals very neatly with the problem; allow eight to twelve buds per square metre of *Lebensraum* for each vine. This effectively compensates for the discrepancy between wide and narrow spacing, where root competition is an important factor. The natural vigour of the plant, the choice of the rootstock, the quality of the soil and the prevailing climate will finally determine the number of buds to be left.

The fruiting canes intended for the following year must be chosen with great care. At the end of the season vines appear as a thicket of growth, most of which has to be cut off and reduced to a manageable size. The problem is, of course, what to cut off and what to leave.

The first consideration is to retain well-ripened wood, for only such canes will be really fruitful. Some *Vitis vinifera* varieties are notoriously reluctant to ripen shoots produced during indifferent summers, and in England these occur all too frequently. Selected canes should therefore be copper-coloured over much of their length and free from fungous diseases. Botrytis and phomopsis manifest themselves by bleaching the canes and covering them with black spots.

Care should be taken to avoid choosing thick shoots with buds produced abnormally far apart; this indicates that the vine is absorbing too much nitrogen and making growth that will not ripen properly. At the same time a fruiting cane must not be too thin and therefore lacking sufficient reserves of energy; ideally, it should be as thick as a pencil, with buds at intervals of about 4 inches only.

It is better to retain shoots close to the main stem if they have fulfilled the considerations mentioned above; these make the most suitable fruiting canes. Unfortunately, vines tend to be vigorous at the summit of their growth; for this reason it has been found beneficial to arch the fruiting canes, so as to promote vigour where it is most needed. If it should prove impracticable to retain one of the basal shoots, there is a real danger that the old wood may sooner or later have to be cut back in order to prevent the main stem from growing longer and longer. Ideally, the stem should remain about 4 inches below the wire to which the fruiting cane is attached or, if the cane is arched, not more than 6 inches above the wire to which the end is anchored.

Cutting back the old wood in order to restore the shape of a vine should be avoided if possible. It has to be done from time to time, otherwise the plant becomes unmanageable and difficult to adapt to the wire trellis. The old wood, made up of the stem and (if it exists) the cordon extension, acts as a storehouse for the vines, creating reserves of nutrition, which, if interfered with, will sap its ability to cope with adverse conditions. It has also been confirmed that vines cannot easily repair the wounds inflicted on them if such measures have to be taken.

Having decided exactly what to retain as next year's fruiting wood, the surplus should be cut off, not too close to the selected cane but leaving a short piece measuring about 1/10 inch, over which the cane must be bent and attached to the wire trellis. A bend in the opposite direction could result in a break and should therefore be avoided.

Growers who choose the Guyot system must decide whether to keep one long fruiting cane, a choice that suits varieties which successfully ripen their wood in poor summers, or to prefer a short cane growing on either side of the main stem. The two methods are known as Single Guyot and Double Guyot respectively. The climate of Britain is likely to make the double fruiting cane a more attractive proposition, and English vignerons are usually recommended to adopt this method if they want a better yield.

Apart from the fruiting wood, it is prudent to keep a replacement spur, in the hope that it will provide a healthy cane for the following season. Ideally, this should be formed from a fairly vigorous shoot that has propitiously grown at a slightly lower level than the canes chosen for fruiting. It should be pruned to two buds.

February is the best month for pruning, when the danger from severe winter frosts have receded. Unfortunately, this allows little time to complete the job before bud burst, and if the vineyard is large, many growers prefer to start earlier. As soon as the foliage has been withered by the autumn frost, which in England takes place about the middle of November, pruning can start. It should then be possible to ascertain how much wood has ripened sufficiently to survive. A green core, clearly visible when the wood is cut, indicates which shoots have been unaffected by frost; new growth at the extremities, which has not had time to ripen properly, will be brown and dead.

Old vines that become badly out of shape or severely damaged by winter frosts may have to be rejuvenated. This is usually done by finding a water shoot sprouting from the main stem and allowing it to serve as a replacement. Ideally, it should be about 4 inches above the ground, growing vigorously enough to form a mature cane by the end of the season. If this can be successfully achieved, the new growth should be treated as a young plant, keeping the stem vertical and disbudded, while allowing any additional length to be attached to a horizontal wire. The old trunk must then be removed, if necessary with a saw, but not too close to the new shoot or future growth will be weakened. If, however, the water shoot fails to produce the required vigour, it is perfectly possible to prune back to a couple of buds, as might be recommended with a newly planted vine.

Leaf Control

Left unattended, a healthy vine will produce a mass of foliage. Much of this will be removed by pruning in the winter, but the new growth appearing in the spring must also be controlled. Fruiting buds on wood produced in the previous year will visibly swell and burst into leaf; in Britain this usually occurs at the beginning of May. At the same time, however, shoots tend to appear on the main stem or trunk which, if allowed to remain, would obscure the light and interfere with the free circulation of air. In addition, these water shoots, as they are called, are nearly always sterile and bear no fruit. It is important to remove them as soon as possible before they become established enough to cause a wound when rubbed off. The longer they remain, the more energy will be required to support them, a diversion which the vine can ill afford to undertake.

Nevertheless, there are circumstances in which the retention of a water shoot is to be recommended. Sometimes a vine gets out of shape. Well-ripened wood, suitable for selection as fruiting canes, does not always grow conveniently close to the main stem. In such cases it is often possible to preserve one or even two water shoots capable of providing adequate canes for the following year. In the case of die-back or wilt, it is sometimes possible to find a water shoot close to the ground and to build up an entirely new plant from the roots.

Vines are inclined to produce shoots which are unfruitful. As soon as they have been identified, these should be removed in order to divert energy into those bearing fruit. The reduction of foliage will also help to aerate the leaf canopy and will prevent an outbreak of fungous disease.

As the season advances and the shoots develop into canes, it will be necessary to anchor them to a wire trellis if the Guyot method of training has been adopted. Sooner or later comes a time when the leaders extend beyond the ultimate wire and run the risk of being snapped off by the wind. It is, however, unwise to trim the tops too early in the year; premature treatment of this kind results in the development of vigorous side shoots, which cause an even denser leaf canopy. In northern Europe the middle of August is considered to be the best time to use the shears; in Britain the operation can be delayed until the end of the month.

Experiments carried out in Switzerland show that grapes benefit from the presence of up to thirteen leaves beyond a bunch; it has therefore been recommended that nine leaves should be retained in order to help the fruit attain the optimum degree of maturity. Clearly, this will prove difficult if the posts and wire work are too low, especially if provision has to be allowed for bird netting.

It will be seen therefore that leaves play a very important part in the quality of the must, especially in the United Kingdom, where sunshine is limited and should be exploited to the best possible advantage. In spite of this, a timely check on excessive growth should provide sufficient energy to ripen the fruit and harden enough wood for the production of fruit in the following year.

It will be apparent after the veraison that leaves at the base of each shoot are beginning to turn yellow, wither and die. It is well worth while removing these, and indeed a few more, where they hide the bunches. Such foliage has ceased to make a useful contribution and, if left intact, will impede the circulation of air, causing the fruit to remain permanently wet after a shower or heavy dew. It is possible to remove four or five of the lower leaves without devaluing the ripening process, and the advantage gained by avoiding botrytis helps to justify a somewhat laborious operation. A further bonus will become apparent during the harvest; bunches of grapes are much easier to pick when they are visible, so the vineyard will be stripped in a fraction of the time.

The Arched Fruiting Cane

It is a well-known fact that a vine concentrates most of its energy at the summit of its growth. This being the case, it has been found beneficial to manipulate the fruiting canes in such a way as to ensure that vigorous shoots are to be found where they are most needed. Bending or arching is of some importance if the plants are to be trained on a wire trellis in accordance with the Guyot system. A skilfully treated fruiting cane results in an even distribution of sap, with the most powerful shoots close to the main stem. These can then be effectively retained for the following year if no replacement spur has been able to provide suitable wood.

After removing the old cane, the selected shoot should, if possible, be bent in the same direction—that is to say, directly over the pruning cut—so as to avoid any risk of breakage. It is advisable to ease the wood into the required shape by gently moving the thumbs of each hand from side to side, in order to prevent exerting too violent a pressure at any one place. The end of the new fruiting cane must be attached to a horizontal wire set at a lower level. Provided the buds at the base of the shoot are allowed to occupy a superior position, they have a good chance of producing strong, healthy wood during the following season.

It is important to make sure that the horizontal wires are really taut, especially those which support the cane; simple devices are available that allow the tension to be adjusted, and where appropriate these should be fitted to each row before the wire trellis has been completed. Wires that sag under pressure are unable to fulfil their proper function.

Another factor should be taken into account. Tethering a vine, or bending upright growth, in order to make it go sideways subjects the plant to some degree of stress, and this is likely to distort its shape. It is therefore desirable, particularly with young vines, to bind the stems to a vertical stake in two or three places with plastic or raffia. The ties should not be too tight, nor should they be allowed to remain after the stem starts to swell, otherwise the flow of sap will be restricted.

A period of damp weather should be chosen for manipulating the fruiting canes prior to bud burst. It should, of course, follow the pruning operation, but if this has taken place earlier, it can be delayed until the spring.

6

Training Methods

The Guyot System

This method of training vines has many advantages and is generally considered to be the most suitable for Western Europe. It has been installed and elaborated in various ways, with the object of improving both quality and yield, but in principle it has always followed the original pattern. It requires a wire trellis supported by posts made of wood, metal or concrete, to which the fruiting canes of the vine are attached in such a way as to prevent damage from the wind. In order to achieve this, the vine is encouraged to develop a permanent vertical stem or trunk, from which one or two horizontal or arched canes are preserved each year to bear the fruiting buds for the following season. The shoots that develop from these buds are secured to the wire trellis and produce one or more clusters of flowers that become bunches of fruit in the autumn. One or two well-ripened canes are selected from the abundant growth produced to serve as replacements; these should be as close as possible to the main stem. The rest of the wood is removed, with the exception perhaps of two or three buds which might grow out and act as suitable fruiting canes in the year after.

In its simplest form the Guyot system consists of a vertical stem, 4 inches above which runs the lowest horizontal wire of the trellis. A single fruiting cane, saved from the previous year's growth, is bent at right angles where it meets the wire, so that it can be attached to it with fasteners or plaited round it. The cane will have been shortened to carry the right number of buds (about twelve) and must not be allowed to extend beyond the adjacent vine. On no account should the stem be permitted to reach the wire or rise above it; should this occur, it will be necessary to find

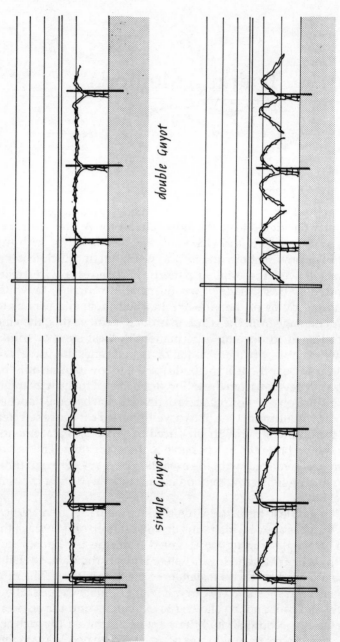

single Guyot

double Guyot

6. The Guyot training system

a water shoot at a convenient height and to reduce the stem to its normal size.

This method of training has come to be known as the Single Guyot system. Double Guyot simply means training two horizontal fruiting canes instead of one. This clearly leaves less space and reduces the number of buds on each side of the plant by half. In this case the top of the stem must be kept at least 6 inches below the bottom wire and is usually forked in order to take two fruiting canes. Some growers feel they get better results with the Double Guyot system, and this may be true in the United Kingdom, where the wood may be reluctant to ripen during inclement seasons, although much will be determined by the character of the vine. Some varieties with brittle wood may be rather difficult to train in this way, and care must be exercised when bending the wood, which will continue to operate satisfactorily with a greenstick fracture.

An alternative method, favoured by some growers, can be achieved by using two horizontal wires, one above and one below the top of the stem for the support of the fruiting canes. These are looped over the upper wire and secured at the tips to the lower wire, producing the L-shape rather than an arch. The two wires need to be at least 1 foot apart. The choice of single or double canes will again remain with the grower, who will be influenced by the type of vine, the vigour of the rootstock and the nature of the soil.

There are certain advantages to this method. Although growth from the buds tends to be irregular, there must be room for more of them in the allotted space. Varieties that are shy about setting their fruit are likely to benefit from the restricted flow of sap, and the wood is said to ripen better.

The top of the stem or trunk should be kept at least 6 inches below the top wire; if it creeps up to the same level, the usual methods must be employed to reduce its height. A gap of 2–3 inches between the canes of adjacent vines is a good insurance against fungous diseases.

An extended version of the Double Guyot system, better known in Germany as Pendelbogen, is defined by keeping longer fruiting canes and securing them in a sweeping arch. This allows room for more buds, and as a consequence the rows must be wider apart. This method is virtually a compromise between

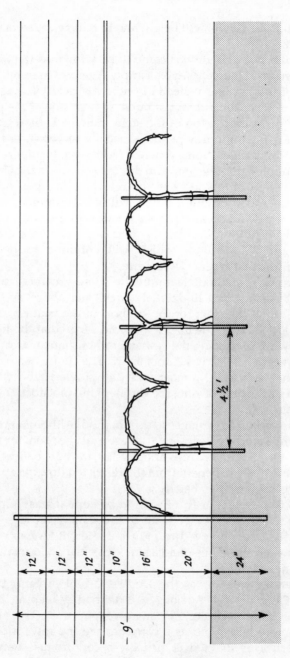

7. Pendelbogen training

high-culture systems and the Double Guyot, as it attempts to increase the yield without substantially reducing the number of vines per acre. The distance between the rows need not exceed 6 feet to 6 feet 6 inches, with the plants spaced as close as 4 feet to 4 feet 3 inches from each other. The stem should not be allowed to exceed 2 feet 9 inches in height, giving a leaf canopy of about 6 feet. The fruiting canes are arched over a wire 3 feet from the ground and secured to another at a height of 1 foot 8 inches. The shoots which develop from the extremities of these canes are allowed to dangle freely; the remainder are trained vertically in the usual way.

The Pendelbogen system is helpful where growth is vigorous and the potential yield generous; it is possible to retain up to twelve fruiting buds on each cane.

The Lenz Moser High-Culture System

Professor Dr Lenz Moser, to give him his full title, came from a family of Austrian vignerons who owned property at Rohrendorf near Krems in the Danube valley. Close by is the fortress of Dürnstein, where Richard I of England was imprisoned and held to ransom during the twelfth century.

Lenz Moser was not prepared to accept the theories relating to viticulture that for centuries had been accepted throughout Austria and in the greater part of Europe. In his book *Weinbau einmal anders* he gives twelve reasons for rejecting the standard methods and explains why he decided to break with tradition.

As early as 1924 he started experimenting with what has now come to be known as the high-culture system, and by 1936 he had planted 30 acres, thus showing full confidence in the techniques he had invented. At first his revolutionary ideas were not favourably received; however, they were gradually adopted not only in the local areas but also finally by the state itself, which gave its formal approval by recommending the system as a satisfactory alternative to those already in use.

The Lenz Moser method is aimed essentially at saving labour and using machinery to the best advantage. By providing more space, the vigneron not only allows the vine freedom of growth, and therefore more fruit, but also permits the passage of standard tractors along the rows. Lenz Moser claims that only one-fifth of the man hours are necessary to manage a vineyard laid out

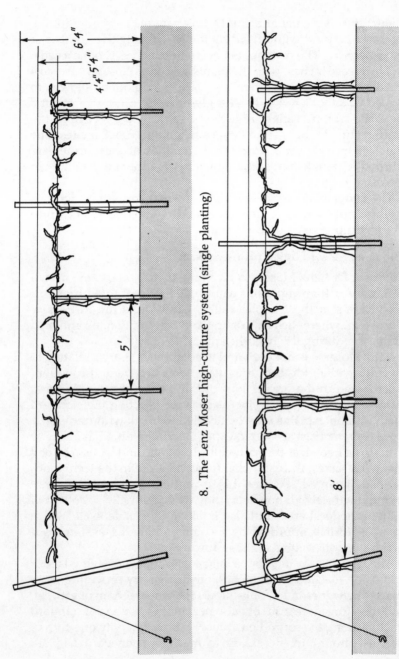

8. The Lenz Moser high-culture system (single planting)

9. The Lenz Moser high-culture system (double planting)

according to his principles. The system required fewer vines, fewer posts and less wire, offering a considerable reduction in the capital cost.

After years of research Moser concluded that the distance between the rows should measure not less than 11 feet, with the vines planted 4 feet 6 inches to 5 feet apart, depending on the vigour of the variety.

The vines are trained on a framework or wire trellis 6 feet 6 inches high. It consists of galvanized wire stretched between 8- foot posts, buried 1 foot 6 inches in the ground, at distances of 20 feet from each other. Three horizontal wires are secured at heights of 4 feet 4 inches, 5 feet 4 inches and 6 feet 4 inches, the lowest of them reserved for the cordon which will bear the season's vegetative growth. The upper wires can with advantage be double in order to contain about a third of the growing shoots, the remainder being allowed to hang down on each side. Moser advocates the use of Voest galvanized-metal posts to support the framework, with a wooden stake for each individual vine.

After planting the first consideration is to develop a straight trunk, and this, of course, may take more than a year. As soon as growth has reached the lowest wire the horizontal fruiting cordon may be formed, and this must be pruned in a special way. Moser recommends alternative cane and spur pruning along the established cordon and suggests that the canes be pruned to six, eight or ten buds according to the capacity of the plant. Vines giving heavy yields with large berries are usually pruned rather more severely than varieties bearing small grapes.

The Geneva Double Curtain

This is a training system recommended by Nelson Shaulis of the Geneva Research Station in New York State. Before considering it, the reader must be reminded that American vines produce shoots that have a tendency to hang downwards, while the European *Vitis vinifera* has an upright habit and may therefore be less suitable for conversion to this method.

Nevertheless, the system has so far shown promise in the United Kingdom and must therefore be taken into account. The difficulty with all training systems lies in the necessity of exposing the leaves and growing shoots as much as possible to the sun; some of the American methods have been found

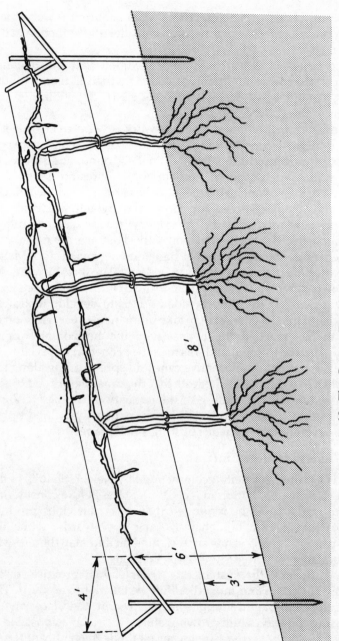

10. The Geneva Double Curtain

wanting in this respect. It was with this in mind that the Geneva Double Curtain system was evolved, enabling the yield per acre to be substantially increased. Ideal for varieties such as Concord, Delaware and Catawba, some modification may nevertheless have to be found for the French and German vines likely to be planted in England.

The Geneva Double Curtain, like the Lenz Moser high-culture system, means fewer plants and wires for the vineyard. It may be assumed that an acre of land devoted to the Geneva Double Curtain method of training will not contain many more than 400 vines, as compared with a possible 2,200 required by orthodox Guyot spacing. The vines are planted 8 feet apart in rows that must be at least 9 feet from each other. Even so this requires the use of a narrow vineyard tractor, and growers may prefer to space the rows at a distance of 12 feet. The wire trellis is supported by posts approximately 35 feet apart and consists of three wires only. The first, to which the vine is attached, is 3 feet from the ground, while the second and third, secured to the extremities of a 4-foot crossbar, support the cordons at nearly twice that height.

The vines will be encouraged to direct their growth on to one or other of these horizontal wires and will therefore be able to occupy up to 16 feet of the wire trellis, providing a foliage curtain which will hang down on either side of the supporting wire. The best results are obtained if the vines are allowed to produce two trunks; in this case there should be no difficulty in covering the available space with fruit-bearing cordons. Dividing the leaf canopies in this way ensures that the area of shade will be substantially reduced.

One of the main advantages for the Geneva Double Curtain is the reduction of labour, which could be of supreme importance today, when the survival of English vineyards is likely to depend on the viability of viticulture as a commercial enterprise. An important operation which cannot, however, be eliminated is the so-called 'shoot positioning', which must be performed manually. This involves the careful arrangement of the vegetative growth so that it does not form a dense canopy of foliage but instead hangs downward in a vertical position to form the double curtain.

Stout posts of treated wood are required to support the trellis, which is usually composed of number 11 gauge galvanized wire. The crossbar or offset arms can be either of metal or wood and should be able to hold the two curtains at a distance of 4 feet from

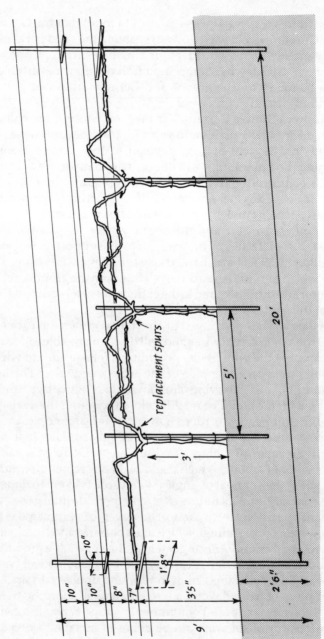

11. The Karl Merz high-culture system

each other. The success of this particular system in the United Kingdom may prove to be due to reasons quite different from those which favour it in New York State. Clearly, it should be tested and scientifically compared with alternative methods of training under the conditions which exist in our maritime climate.

Additional High Culture Methods of Training

Pendelbogen, Geneva Double Curtain and Lenz Moser, all of which adopt a wider spacing between the rows, seem to be the only high-culture systems so far attempted in this country. There are, however, others of a similar nature which should be tested in case they should prove more successful.

One of these is popular in Germany, where it was originally developed by Karl Merz, the owner of a vineyard at Ockenheim, in the province of Rheinhessen. It requires a wire trellis capable of keeping the fruiting canes apart, thus enabling the growing shoots to be separated into three distinct groups. This is achieved by attaching a horizontal batten or 'yoke' to the supporting posts and stapling the length of wire to the extremities. The stem or trunk is kept to a height of 3 feet and then allowed to fork. Subsequent winter pruning results in two short 'prongs' with sufficient buds to produce one fruiting cane and a replacement spur on each 'prong'. The canes, when they have developed, must be arched by bending them over a central wire and attaching them on either side to the wires held apart by the 'yoke'. Each fruiting cane should carry about fifteen buds. Up to half a dozen of the growing shoots are trained vertically; the rest are allowed to hang down on each side, thus dividing them effectively into three groups. A certain amount of defoliation must be undertaken from time to time, particularly if the growth becomes too vigorous. The trailing shoots should be lopped when they touch the ground, leaving a gap of about 6 inches. The vertical growth must also be cut; the time to do this will be at the beginning of September. Each vine requires a stake roughly $\frac{1}{4}$ inch thick, to which it must be securely attached at appropriate intervals. The wire trellis is supported by 9-foot stakes spaced at a distance of 20 feet; the rows themselves must be kept at least 8 feet 6 inches apart.

Another high-culture system, developed in Austria, consists of maintaining four short fruiting canes on a permanent cordon. As with the method devised by Karl Merz, the new growth is divided

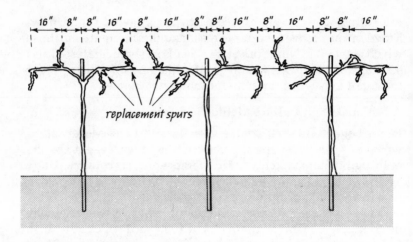

replacement spurs

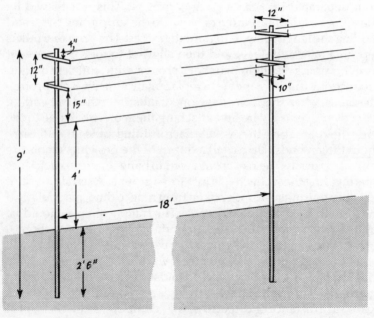

12. The Cane-and-Spur high-culture system

into three groups, one of which is secured by a wire trellis in a vertical position, with the other two trailing naturally on either side.

The vine is allowed to reach a height of 3 feet before being encouraged to fork. The objective is then to produce a permanent cordon by training two canes along a horizontal wire situated 4 feet above the ground. These canes must be pruned back to a distance of 2 feet from the main stem.

On this permanent structure, which will take three or four years to establish, four fruiting shoots should be allowed to develop (two on either side of the stem) and these must not be secured in any way. Spaced roughly 16 inches apart, they are grown from buds on each side of the cordon, so that they sprout in opposite directions. In this way the foliage of the following season can be effectively divided and draped on either side of the row. After pruning they should be furnished with six or seven buds and a replacement spur, with one visible bud, growing if possible from the axil.

During the following season the replacement spur will sprout not only from the visible bud but also from the axil, making two brand-new shoots, with which the whole process can be repeated. The fruiting canes are not secured after pruning because they are inclined to weep automatically as soon as the leaves and flower clusters begin to appear. This causes the basal shoots to grow more vigorously and facilitates the fastening of these in a vertical position.

As might be expected, rigid leaf control must be exercised. No shoots other than those intended for fruit production must be allowed to grow. Any buds trying to sprout between the four that have been selected should immediately be rubbed out, together with such water shoots as are not actually required for replacement purposes. There ought to be a gap of 8 inches between the end of one cordon and the beginning of the next; this will allow an adequate circulation of air round the plants.

Each vine must be attached to a stake that is strong enough to keep it straight, and the wire trellis is usually supported by posts furnished with one or two small crosspieces; these serve to hold the vertical shoots together and thus divide the foliage into three distinct groups.

Growing Vines on Walls

> Close bosom-friend of the maturing sun;
> Conspiring with him how to load and bless
> With fruit the vines that round the thatch-eaves run. . . .
>
> John Keats, 'To Autumn'

Lines like this may have helped to create a desire, which the English with their love of gardening have undoubtedly fostered, to train a vine on the walls of houses. The plant should derive benefit from the protection afforded, it is thought, and to a certain extent should thrive on the reflected heat. Unfortunately, any such endeavours, though laudable, have too often been disappointed; the reason for failure has seldom been difficult to find.

Until quite recently nurserymen have been unable to cater for anyone proposing to plant vines out of doors. Such has been the belief that vines can thrive only in a greenhouse, and that grapes are cultivated only for the purpose of eating, that nurseries have tended to confine their stock to specimens of Black Hamburg and Muscat of Alexandra. Such varieties are practically useless outside, particularly in the colder parts of the country.

Nurserymen, of course, who want to sell their plants, will insist that these vines will produce fruit successfully on a south-facing wall. Although many of them have now begun to stock varieties that do not require glass, it may be safer to consult an independent source before choosing a plant that is going to occupy valuable space for a number of years.

It is a fallacy to suppose that grapes suitable for the production of wine have little or no importance for the table. Greenhouse grapes are clearly more acceptable as a commercial proposition, but that is no reason why some excellent fruit cannot be produced out of doors, either in the vineyard or on a wall. It is simply a matter of choosing the right variety.

The following vines should regularly produce a satisfactory yield in the United Kingdom. Although they can be cultivated for wine, their fruit is equally good for the table: Madeleine Royale, Perle von Czaba, Müller-Thurgau, Huxelrebe, Bouviertraube, Königin von Weingarten, Seyval Blanc, Frühburgunder, Leon Millot, Muscat Bleu (83/2).

Those who want to grow vines on their houses will usually choose vertical or horizontal cordons. The choice will clearly be dictated by the size of the wall and the location of the windows. Any vast expanse of brickwork, such as may often be found on a garden wall, can be effectively and economically covered by a series of horizontal cordons, if necessary trained at separate levels.

The vines themselves can be spaced at distances up to 12 or 13 feet, with sufficient capacity to cover the area in a limited period. Fruit is borne on spurs which are cut back annually to two or three buds. Care should be taken to develop spurs only on the upper side of the fruiting cane if a horizontal cordon has been chosen. Those on the lower side are never wholly satisfactory, and if they have to be removed at a later stage, some damage can be done to the flow of sap. They should therefore be rubbed off as buds, before they have the opportunity to form spurs. Ideally, the spurs should be spaced at intervals of about 9 inches, and the shoots which develop from them should be pruned every year to a maximum of two buds. During the following season these buds ought to produce a couple of canes, the lower of which should be preserved by reducing to two buds and the upper completely removed. The horizontal cordon can be extended each year, but only by a modest length, which should not exceed 18 inches. The extension should be made from a bud situated on the underside of the cane.

Vertical cordons are clearly more suitable on walls where space is limited. It is possible, for example, to train a vine in such a way as to provide two vertical cordons on either side of a window; this can be done by centring the plant immediately below the window, allowing the trunk to form and grow two arms that can be directed to the appropriate place. Horizontal cordons can also be trained on a high wall at two levels. This should be better than attempting to cover the area with an espalier. Vines tend to devote most of their energy to the extremities of their growth, providing these are situated furthest from the ground; hence the arching that is a prominent feature of so many methods of training. It is therefore better to alternate cordons at different levels and to overlap if the wall is deep enough to provide sufficient space.

Some varieties are not suitable for spur pruning, as they are reluctant to provide fruit of the basal buds. If this happens to be the case, it is advisable to leave up to five buds on each spur; this could, of course, produce an excessive number of leaves and make defoliation an essential undertaking.

Spur pruning can also be used for vines trained on a pergola, where the foliage may serve as a sunshade, allowing the fruit to hang down in decorative bunches. As this has been done in bistros all over the Continent, it is surprising to find that it has seldom been copied in this country.

7

Diseases of the Vine

Virus Diseases

From time to time concern has been expressed about the incidence of virus diseases and how they could find their way into our young English vineyards. Since it has been established that most of them are caused by propagation—through either infected scions used for grafting or rooted cuttings—some growers have demanded stricter phytosanitary controls on the import of vines from foreign countries. Others have already identified symptoms which point to the fact that an invasion has already taken place.

It should not be assumed, however, that every substandard vine is suffering from a virus disease just because it fails to produce a normal crop. Many reasons can be found to explain the stunted growth and miserable yield so often attributed to a virus infection, and the vigneron should seek professional advice before jumping to conclusions.

Although virus diseases are widespread through the plant and animal kingdom, little was known about their effect on vines until this century. Plant viruses are extremely small and represent particles of nucleic acids which can exist only in a living cell.Their presence upsets the metabolism of the cell and produces deformities of growth, reduced yields and, in certain cases, death of the plant itself. Some of these diseases have reached Europe from America; at the same time some are no doubt being imported from the Continent and becoming established in the United Kingdom. During the last few years a number of them have been identified, and the grower should endeavour to recognize the symptoms and adopt what counter-measures he thinks fit.

Apart from propagation by budding or grafting, virus diseases can be transmitted by nematodes in the soil or by aerial vectors. In view of the fact that the trouble is usually disseminated by infected scions, there would seem to be good reason to scrutinize even more closely the plants that come into this country from abroad. Just such a system of control has been introduced by the State of California, where imported vines are 'indexed' to make sure that they are virus-free. Whether a similar examination can be adopted here is doubtful, but growers may wish to import their stock from suppliers who at any rate claim to handle only virus-free stock.

For the English grower the danger of importing infected stock persists; whether or not this justifies the exclusion of suppliers who cannot guarantee the offer of virus-free vines is open to question.

Court-noué

Often loosely used to describe a range of virus diseases, the name 'court-noué' can be more accurately referred to as grape fan-leaf virus, which is the title conferred on it by the Americans. The French have another word for it, *dégénérescence infectieuse* and in Germany it is known as *Reisigkrankheit*. It is clearly a troublesome virus in Europe and the one most likely to find its way into our English vineyards. Propagation by infected stock is the main cause of its dissemination, but it can also be transmitted through the soil by the nematode *Xiphinema index*.

The most important symptom is perhaps represented by the deformed condition of the foliage. The leaf, as the English name suggests, assumes the appearance of a half-closed fan by folding upwards and inwards around the central vein. At the same time the margin becomes more jagged, with fewer and deeper serrations.

Not only are the leaves distorted but also certain abnormalities occur in other parts of the vine. Internodes can be irregular in length; some are so short as to be nonexistent, creating the illusion of a double bud. Tendrils appear in odd places and behave in a peculiar fashion. Early in the season there is a tendency for shoots to zigzag at the nodes; growth is also poor but soon improves dramatically. It is not unusual for the leaves to show some kind of mottling, with patches of paler green that seem to come from the veins. Petioles can fork and produce two leaves; in addition, the shoot itself can divide or even produce a number of weak, slender canes that are said to resemble a broomhead.

As a direct result of the virus infection, yield is severely affected; the flower clusters fail to set properly and the canes mature prematurely. For some time it was thought that the virus was transmitted by the phylloxera aphis, but this theory was subsequently discounted. In addition to the nematode mentioned above, another (*Circonemoides xenoplas*) was considered to be suspect, but no conclusive evidence has so far been forthcoming. Infected soil, however, is able to perpetuate the disease and may continue to do so for a number of years. It would therefore be unwise to replace a vine that shows any of the symptoms referred to above without treating the area with a suitable nematicide like dichloropropane+dichloropropene.

Yellow Mosaic

Yellow mosaic, or panaschure as it is known in Europe, is one of the more common virus diseases and may well have some significance for the English grower. It is usually spread by budding and grafting and could therefore be imported from France and Germany, where it has been indigenous for years. It can also be transmitted by a nematode known as *Xiphinema index* and will remain active in the soil for some time after infected vines have been removed.

As the name suggests, the disease manifests itself by a discoloration of the leaves, which become pale green, yellow or even white. The nature of the symptoms, however, is far from constant. Sometimes the leaves are mottled and the shoots turn yellow; sometimes the discoloration is confined to the veins and their immediate vicinity; and sometimes, as the season advances, whole areas of the leaf appear to be blanched.

The virus is not a killer but is quite able to impede growth and seriously reduce the yield. The French regard yellow mosaic as a form of court-noué and tend to include vein banding and asteroid mosaic under the same heading. Certain *Vitis vinifera* varieties favoured in France, such as Chardonnay and Aramon, are more vulnerable than others, although none of the European vines is immune.

Flavescence dorée

There seems to be some uncertainty about whether the virus responsible for this disease is the same as that known in the United States as 'corky bark'. In France it is also described as *maladie du Baco* because of its effect on Baco 22A. It was located in Armagnac round about the middle of the twentieth century, a little later in Germany, where it is sometimes known as 'goldene Vergilbung'. It may never be of concern to the English grower because of its dissemination by an aerial vector, *Scaphoideus littoralis*, a member of the cicada group of insects, which so far seems not to have invaded our shores.

As the name suggests, the disease is made manifest by a vivid yellowing of the foliage. This is usually accompanied by some degree of leaf roll towards the end of the summer. The young wood splits along its length and becomes brittle and spongy in appearance. It is unable to ripen in the approved fashion. The grapes are small and often irregular in size, and they have a nasty taste. As the season advances, they wither and fall. Subsequent seasons are characterized by a general loss of vigour.

Perhaps the most effective method of control is to use an insecticide powerful enough to exterminate cicada insects.

Grape Leaf Roll Virus

The symptoms of this virus disease, known in France as *enroulement* and in Germany as *Rollkrankheit*, are sometimes attributed to vines suffering from potassium deficiency; it can, however, be distinguished by observing that the virus first causes damage to the lower leaves of the shoot, whereas a lack of potassium affects younger foliage.

Leaf roll has existed in Europe for centuries. In California, however, it is widespread and was originally identified as White Emperor disease because the fruit of the Emperor vine failed to turn colour at harvest time. American vines do not show exactly the same symptoms as those which occur in Europe, and growers should remember that similar conditions may be induced by causes other than that of leaf roll virus.

Infected stock may show signs of the disease in July. The oldest leaves begin to curve downwards at the margin, and this deformity gradually spreads upwards to affect the younger foliage on each shoot. At the same time the vine starts prematurely to assume an autumn colouring and fails to achieve the normal production of sugar. Yield is also affected and, with certain varieties, vigour of growth is sapped. Towards the end of the season the leaves become puffy-looking, with sunken veins, and may turn colour, assuming a scalded appearance.

As already stated, leaf roll and the symptoms that accompany it can be caused by a potassium deficiency, by the activities of certain insects or even by the nature of the soil which, if heavy and soggy, could stifle the roots of the vines planted in it. To determine whether a virus is responsible, suspected stock can be grafted and examined to discover whether the same symptoms are being reproduced, for the disease is faithfully transmitted by propagation.

Pierce's Disease

This is a native of California, where it was identified as a virus disease nearly fifty years ago. It has now spread to all the southern part of the United States and is believed to have appeared in Australia and the Argentine. So far it has not been reported in Europe, which is just as well, as it can be lethal to *Vitis vinifera*. Infected cuttings and grafts are unable to root properly, so the disease is unlikely to be spread by propagation; instead this virus is transmitted by aerial vectors, principally insects of the cicada family, of which there are three that are mainly responsible.

The disease apparently affects a number of weeds and grasses, including a variety of shrub. Lucerne is especially vulnerable, and the virus is known to cause alfalfa dwarf. Vineyards which are set in close proximity to certain species of plants are more likely to suffer from virus infection, particularly if the weather has been warm and humid.

In the summer months the condition can be recognized by leaf burn, which usually starts at the margin and works its way towards the petiole. As the season advances, the leaves turn completely brown and, in severe cases, may even fall off the stalk. The grapes tend to colour prematurely and then wither; growth can be severely impeded, and the wood fails to become properly ripe.

Vines suffering from Pierce's disease often survive for two or three years. In subsequent seasons their growth is affected, and the leaves become mottled as a result of chlorosis. Burning and scalding are prominent features, and the fruit withers before it is ready to pick. The plant finally succumbs, although it may take up to five years to do so.

Additional Virus Diseases

Textbooks quote other virus diseases, some of which may find their way into English vineyards. The problem of identification could be difficult, especially where the symptoms lack consistency in different varieties. It is true to say that a virus that has become established in America can behave quite differently in Europe; even in adjacent countries the manifestations may not be identical. It is therefore better to describe the symptoms as they have been reported.

Yellow Vein

A virus disease said to be confined to California. As it can be disseminated by budding or grafting, it may be only a matter of time before its presence is reported in Europe. The varieties Carignan and Grenache are the principal victims, but it is also known to affect others. Where inflorescence has already taken place, however rare this may prove to be, the bunches of grapes appear sparse and incomplete. The leaf symptoms are not always easy to see, as they are usually confined to a section of the plant. They tend to appear late in the season and are often to be found at the lower end of the shoot. They take the form of chrome-yellow blemishes, which run along the veins of the leaf like a tapestry. The disease is also said to be transmitted by a nematode known as *Xiphinema americanum*.

Asteroid Mosaic

Although this disease produces symptoms that might be mistaken for others of a similar nature, the virus is distinguished by the star-like patches that appear on the leaves. These are caused by a transparency of the veins, which can run together and form translucent areas. The leaves become brittle and asymmetrical and often show blisters that retain their normal colour. The virus can be transmitted by budding or grafting, and vines affected by this disease bear little or no fruit.

Vein Banding

This disease is manifested by the appearance of light-green or chrome-yellow bands along the veins of the older leaves. The symptoms occur in the late summer and are accompanied by coulure, which affects the flower cluster and prevents the berries from setting properly. The virus can be transmitted both by nematodes and by grafting.

In addition to the virus diseases already listed, there are others which have been identified and reported from various sources. Among these should be included virus-like diseases that have not yet been isolated; some confusion still exists with regard to the names by which they can be internationally recognized and, as a result, some duplication of titles is a possibility. They include: peach rosette mosaic, yellow speckle, spindle shoot, Hungarian chrome yellow mosaic, corky bark and marble mosaic.

8

Fungous Diseases

Plasmopara Viticola

Also known as *Peronospora viticola*. In England it goes by the name of 'downy mildew'; the French call it *le mildiou* and the Germans sometimes refer to it as *falscher Mehltau*.

Like some other cryptogamic diseases, it was imported from the United States. It appeared in France in 1878 and soon spread all over Europe. During the early part of the present century it reached South Africa, Australia, New Zealand and the Argentine and indeed has penetrated almost every wine-producing country in the world. In Europe downy mildew is considered to be the most dangerous of all fungous diseases, although this opinion has yet to be shared by English growers, who are much more concerned with the incidence of *Botrytis cinerea*. Certainly it would seem from reports so far received that powdery mildew is a menace more frequently found in the modest acreage already under cultivation.

This could well be due to the microclimate, although optimum conditions for the development of oidium seem less likely to exist in the United Kingdom, whereas those which favour the growth of peronospora could prevail at any time during the course of a normal English summer. For this malady thrives on humidity and moisture, caused by rainfall, dew and fog. It can develop at any temperature between 10 and 30 °C (50–86 °F) but flourishes at an optimum ranging from 20 to 25 °C.

The fungus attacks all the green parts of the vine—buds, leaves, tendrils, flowers and grapes before the veraison; it will also affect the growing canes until such time as they have ripened, and at the end of the season the spores will overwinter in fallen leaves and other debris scattered over the vineyard. The

European *Vitis vinifera* is especially vulnerable to the disease, whereas certain American varieties such as *V. riparia*, *V. rupestris* and *V. berlandieri* can offer a greater degree of resistance. Young vineyards are more likely to be affected, and particular care should be taken during the first year, especially in circumstances where the nature of the soil is likely to promote vigorous growth. In the United Kingdom trouble could occur at any time from the end of May; it is therefore important to adopt counter-measures as soon as the leaves are large enough to become infected. This could happen after a heavy shower, provided the temperature is sufficient to encourage the growth of the spores.

The manifestations of the disease are not difficult to identify. The first symptom takes the form of yellowing spots on the surface of the leaves. They have an oily, translucent appearance and are usually accompanied by corresponding patches of mould on the underside of the leaf. The flower trusses become covered with a white fungous growth, and if berries have started to form, they turn blue, shrivel and assume a leathery appearance. Canes affected by the disease fail to ripen in the usual way and are therefore unable to produce fruit during the following season.

The incidence of peronospora is determined largely by climatic conditions. Wet weather, if persistent, is responsible for the infection, which can develop rapidly during the summer months, especially when the temperature is favourable. The incubation period varies from two to three weeks in May to as little as five days in July, so the frequency of preventive spraying must be varied accordingly.

Control

Bordeaux mixture is widely used for the control of peronospora; it has the advantage of being very effective and cheap. It also prevents the development of some other fungous diseases. It has, however, the disadvantage of inhibiting growth, which is why it is seldom used in northern vineyards. It can also damage the leaves and shoots of the vine if used too early in the year and causes coulure if applied during the flowering period. It is therefore better to use the so-called organic fungicides, many of which can be effective against other fungous diseases as well. Antracol (Propineb) helps to control dead arm disease and brenner; Dithane Ultra also inhibits botrytis. Other fungicides recommended for use against downy mildew are Captan (controls botrytis), Zineb (controls dead arm and brenner) and Folpet (which controls all three). There are more, although some of them may not be available in the United Kingdom.

The vines should be sprayed as soon as the leaves measure ⅘ inch in diameter. The frequency of treatment will depend on climatic behaviour. After heavy rainfall it is important to spray within ten days; this generally means at least two or three times before flowering. Many growers are afraid to apply fungicides during the flowering period, but the damage inflicted by peronospora, should it appear, is simply not worth the risk. A cool summer can delay completion, so it is wiser to spray again when three-quarters of the flowering is finished if circumstances demand it. The vine is most vulnerable at this stage; therefore prompt action is very important.

After flowering the treatment is similar, except that some growers prefer to substitute a copper-based fungicide for the final application, in order to protect the fruit from botrytis and to assist the canes to ripen. After the middle of August the danger from peronospora and oidium tends to decline and, as a consequence, regular treatment can be terminated. Although the method is less effective, some growers prefer to dust their vines with the appropriate preparations made up in powder form; as a rough guide 1 cwt of powder will be sufficient for 3 acres.

Oidium Tuckeri

So called because it was found by an English gardener named Tucker; he discovered it in a greenhouse at Margate, where it made its first appearance in Europe. Like other unwelcome visitors, it seems to have been imported from North America. That was in 1845; two years later it was reported to have invaded France. By 1850 it had spread to Spain, Italy and Germany, and now it is no longer confined to Europe and its country of origin but has reached Africa, Australia and South America. Sometimes described as *uncinula necator*, the disease is known in the United States as 'powdery mildew' and in Germany as *echter Mehltau*.

Although all vines can be attacked, some varieties are more vulnerable than others. American strains like *labrusca* and *rupestris* are fairly resistant but certain *viniferas* such as

Cabernet-Sauvignon, Chasselas, Portugieser and Silvaner are regular casualties.

Oidium feeds on all the green parts of a vine but does not seem to affect ripened wood or grapes after the veraison. However, the spores do overwinter in the buds and are ready to break out and multiply during the spring. Known as conidia, they are widely distributed by the wind, by which means they are able to infect the leaves and, later on, the fruit, covering them with a greyish-white powdery mould, as though they had been dusted with flour.

Partially arrested growth is a feature of the disease and often provides an early indication of its presence by causing the leaves to curl. Immature grapes split open, revealing the seeds, because the affected skins are unable to accommodate the swelling pulp. Oidium is not inhibited by cold weather, nor does its development rely on rain or humid conditions. The spores will multiply at a temperature below 10 °C (50 °F), although they prefer a thermometer reading of somewhere between 20 and 30 °C (70–85 °F). Incubation of the spores is completed in anything from seven to twelve days, according to prevailing conditions.

Control

The traditional weapon generally used against oidium is sulphur. This chemical can be applied as a powder or, even more effectively, in soluble form, when it is usually referred to as 'wettable sulphur'. It is important when ordering powdered sulphur to make sure that the product is intended for use in a vineyard; the particles of sulphur should be finely divided in order to ensure complete coverage of the leaf surface and such parts of the new growth that are likely to be vulnerable. The dust should be applied when the weather is warm but not excessively hot; at temperatures below 18 °C (64 °F) its efficiency will be impaired, and in cold weather it will prove to be ineffective. Wettable sulphur is easier to use because it is compatible with fungicides and insecticides and can therefore be applied at the same time. Although the recommended dilution is intended as a preventative measure, wettable sulphur can be used as an eradicant if the concentration is increased. Apart from sulphur, Karathane and Rubigan have proved effective.

Like other fungous diseases, powdery mildew flourishes in areas where the circulation of air is inadequate. If allowed to do so, it invades the greenhouse and usually appears in a vineyard where abundant foliage generates a hot-house atmosphere. It is therefore important to undertake a sensible programme of defoliation where necessary; such a practice will also help to avoid the ravages of botrytis at a later stage.

Bearing in mind that the disease overwinters in the buds, any outbreak is bound to constitute a threat for the following year. It is therefore wise to adopt counter-measures immediately after bud burst and before the dormant spores can multiply and be scattered. Vineyards with a clean bill of health can probably omit sulphur from the first peronospora spray, provided it is included subsequently. Wettable sulphur is marketed in the United Kingdom under a variety of brand names.

Botrytis Cinerea

In France botrytis is known as *la pourriture grise*, unless it produces that special flavour that characterizes the wines of Sauternes; it is then referred to as *la pourriture noble*. The same distinction is evident in other countries; thus we find 'grey rot' or 'noble rot' in English and *Grauschimmel* or *Edelfäule* in the German language. The disease is much feared in the United Kingdom, where excessive humidity and misty conditions can cause it to flourish.

Botrytis is not exclusive to the vine. It is ubiquitous and affects all manner of plants. Strawberries, tomatoes and potatoes, for instance, all suffer the ravages of this disease unless appropriate action is taken at the right time. Gardeners are familiar with the damage caused to these and other favourite crops and are obliged to take the necessary counter-measures.

The incidence of botrytis varies each year according to the moods of the climate. A long period of drought followed by heavy rain, such as occurred in England during the summer of 1976, create ideal conditions; the inevitable surge of sap causing some of the berries to split, accompanied by prolonged wet weather, ensures a rapid development of destructive mycelium with an all too premature harvest as a consequence.

The disease thrives on damp conditions but, unlike downy mildew, is able to flourish at lower temperatures. Although infection spreads rapidly between 15 and 20 °C (about 60–70 °F) it can also develop at temperatures just above freezing point, although at a slower rate. It is known to attack all the growing parts of the vine—leaves, shoots, flower trusses and canes; its presence during the winter can be observed on wood which has failed to ripen and is clearly indicated by black smudges or spots (scelerotia) on canes which have assumed a bleached appearance instead of turning dark brown. The tips of growing shoots, when affected, wilt and die; leaves develop brown patches, mainly at the edges, as though they had been scorched, while the flower trusses wither and just crumble into powder. Canes are also discoloured with a brown streak which eats into the tissues, causing termination of growth.

The most serious damage, however, is caused to the bunches of fruit. Botrytis has a way of striking before the grapes are fully ripe, attacking both the berries themselves and the stalks which connect the bunch to the cane. In order to prevent the disease from spreading, the grower is obliged to harvest his fruit prematurely, with a consequent loss of quality. Stem rot causes the bunches to fall and entails a reduction in yield.

Infection is most likely to start if the berries have suffered bruising from a hailstorm or strong wind; insects can also inflict damage, allowing the fungus to penetrate the skin and spread the disease more rapidly. It has been established, however, that botrytis can attack the fruit without the help of such allies. Untidy flowering provides a breeding ground for the mycelium, which, having established itself, can multiply inside the grape cluster and prove hard to eradicate. The persistence of damp conditions can cause a build-up of spores which are able to puncture the skin when the fruit starts to ripen and become softer. The berries turn first brown and then grey, forming a film of mould which, when disturbed, scatters like dust, broadcasting the infection on all sides.

Control

It is important to remember that the British climate induces conditions that are often more humid than those to be found abroad. Bearing this in mind, it is logical to allow a little more room between plants and wider spacing between the rows. Soil in England is usually fertile, with the result that vigorous growth may cause overcrowding where conventional training methods are used. Popular varieties like Müller-Thurgau should therefore be given a little more latitude in order to provide an adequate circulation of air around the foliage. As botrytis spores are able to multiply as long as damp or wet conditions prevail, it is important for the ripening grapes to dry quickly after a shower or early morning dew. Some defoliation is advisable therefore, in the area where fruit is to be found, in order to let in plenty of light and air. This should be done when the grapes are beginning to ripen— say, when the specific gravity of the must has reached 1050. Below this figure the fungus can attack only damaged fruit, so if insects abound, or if hailstorms occur, defoliation could be started earlier. Up to five leaves at the base of each shoot may be removed without impairing the efficiency of the plant.

Some new fungicides, which are now available on the market, have been successfully used against botrytis. Like Benlate, some of them may prove effective for a short time only, until the disease has built up a resistance, so it may be worth ringing the changes over a period of years. Sumisclex and Ronilan are both powerful but are not recommended for nursery beds, as they tend to burn the foliage. Rovral, which is almost as strong, should be used instead. Elvaron and Benlate are well-tried alternatives but may not be quite as effective under severe conditions.

The most important time to use these sprays is at the conclusion of the flowering period. The vine is vulnerable at this moment and needs protection. Subsequently it is advisable to spray before the berries form a compact bunch in order to ensure adequate penetration by the fungicide. After the fruit has set, spraying should in any case take place at regular intervals and should be terminated only when there is some risk of inhibiting the fermentation. In order to preserve the flower truss, it is wise to consider applying an anti-botrytis spray before flowering commences. Some growers favour two applications, particularly if weather conditions have been unfavourable; others are content to rely on fungicides which control peronospora but are also able to inhibit botrytis.

No account of this disease would be complete without describing the danger it presents to the storage of cuttings intended for bench grafting. The Germans have produced an excellent preparation, marketed under the name Chinosol, which can be used as a disinfectant for American and European wood prior to grafting. Its method of use is discussed under a separate heading (see p. 69–70).

Phomopsis Viticola

The Americans call this malady 'dead arm disease' because of the way it kills a limb of the vine it attacks. It is known in France as *excoriose* and in Germany as *Schwarzfleckenkrankheit*. As with other fungous complaints, it develops after a period of rain. Its presence is perhaps most vividly demonstrated during the winter months, when the canes of an affected plant take on a bleached appearance and are covered with a multitude of round black dots (pycnidia). At first sight the affliction may be confused with the symptoms of botrytis, but the black specks are smaller and much more numerous.

The leaves begin to show the disease in June by way of yellow patches along the veins, each with a dark brown or black centre. As these develop, the leaves turn yellow and die. Similar discoloration can affect the growing shoots, which then flake and split causing damage to the plant tissues. Phomopsis has a way of starting at the base of a shoot and then working its way up. It is not unusual to see evidence of the disease on the first two or three internodes only, leaving the remaining part apparently unaffected. Again, the shoots most likely to be attacked are those which lie near the trunk and are in the most favourable position to provide suitable replacement canes. Unripened wood develops a series of discoloured streaks with mauve edges, which later assume a scabby appearance. Bunches of grapes are less frequently affected, although the stems can turn black and the berries dark blue. Unlike other fungous diseases, phomopsis seems to thrive in cold weather and the pycnidia are well placed to spread the infection during a wet spring. Care should be taken when selecting scion wood for grafting, for the disease can be transmitted to the new stock.

Control

All discarded wood known to be infected with phomopsis should be gathered up and burned as soon as possible after pruning. If the outbreak has been severe, the vines should be sprayed twice, once at the beginning of the winter as soon as pruning has been completed and then again just before bud burst. If only one application is necessary, it is better to choose the spring rather than the early part of the winter in the hope of curtailing further infection. Dinoseb or DNOC are recommended counter-measures, although ordinary tar-oil washes are said to be equally effective and cheaper.

Stem Rot and Stem Atrophy

These disorders affect the stalks responsible for supporting the bunches of grapes and are able to cause serious losses by depositing large quantities of fruit on the ground before the harvest takes place. Each of them can be attributed to a different source, but they both have the same consequence, and every effort should be directed towards preventing their occurrence.

Stem rot is a direct result of botrytis infection and is likely to develop during prolonged periods of wet weather. Should these prevail in the spring at an early date, some of the flower trusses will wither and die, with further decay attacking the stalks. In such conditions it would be wise to apply an anti-botrytis spray before flowering started. Further applications at the recommended intervals are extremely important, for the danger of botrytis infection is always at hand.

Stem atrophy or paralysis is a physiological disorder. It can be caused by an imbalance of plant nutrients, a maladjustment of growing conditions, an unsuitable soil structure or even the wrong sort of rootstock. It manifests itself by the appearance of dark brown discolorations, which grow in size and subsequently encircle the stalk. The plant tissues are affected and are unable to maintain the growth of the fruit, with the result that the grapes shrivel and wither. The general paralysis, with or without the help of botrytis, ends by severing the stalk, allowing the entire bunch to fall on the ground.

The disorder has a way of striking very suddenly when the grapes have reached a specific gravity of 1030 and is not apparently activated by wet weather. The best method of control is to spray the vines at ten-day intervals with a 1 per cent solution of magnesium sulphate. Spraying should commence when the fruit begins to soften. Müller-Thurgau, Chasselas and Riesling vines are vulnerable; of the new varieties Faber is the most likely to suffer.

9

Predatory Insects

Phylloxera Vastatrix

Although the phylloxera aphis has never become established in the United Kingdom, it is not exactly a stranger to our shores. Half a dozen outbreaks occurred in the nineteenth century, and rather more have been reported since. Although these were isolated cases, nearly all of which were found in greenhouses, one or two infestations are understood to have been located in open vineyards. Whether or not it will ever become a real menace on such scattered English sites, as it did in other European countries, remains a matter for conjecture. No book on viticulture, however, would be complete without a description of this damaging pest and the havoc it has caused to wine-producing countries all over the world. Even though it may fail to establish itself in Britain, any reported invasion is bound to result in loss, for the Ministry of Agriculture will be obliged to destroy the infected area immediately, whether or not the vines are grafted on the American rootstocks.

Phylloxera belongs to an order known as the *Hemiptera*, which includes aphides and scale insects. They derive nourishment by sucking the goodness out of growing plants, causing them to waste away over a period of time. In one of its stages of development phylloxera becomes a winged insect, a feature of the order, but differs from the other members by confining its attentions to the *Vitis* family only, instead of being able to survive on substitute diets.

The natural habitat of the phylloxera louse had for centuries been the Mississippi valley, where it existed by feeding on the indigenous vines of the North American continent. Nobody knows exactly when it arrived in Europe or why it took so long to cross the Atlantic. It has been suggested, with some justification, that a contributory cause was the advent of the steamship and the railway, which enabled the pest to survive the journey on imported plants. It has been established that some vine leaves with phylloxera galls were discovered in a Hammersmith greenhouse during the summer of 1863, but entomologists were unable to identify the cause until five years later. Earlier records however show that some French vignerons had begun to notice the symptoms of an unidentifiable disease which appeared to be spreading in the vineyards of southern France. It took a few years for the experts to discover the nature of the trouble; by then it was impossible to stop it from spreading with alarming speed, not only within the country but across the frontiers to other parts of Europe. Despite elaborate precautions, the aphis was found to have invaded Germany in 1874, where it was positively identified in the Rhineland near Bonn. By degrees it penetrated most of the wine-producing countries of the world, causing considerable loss and hardship wherever it became established. Isolated islands like Madeira were unable to claim immunity, and the phylloxera scourge, coming so soon after the oidium disaster, very nearly wiped out the viable production of wine from the island's vineyards.

In France, the gravity of the situation was not fully appreciated at first; possibly the speed at which the insect took control persuaded the French Government in 1873 to offer a reward to anyone who could find an effective way of stopping the rot. The prize was quite substantial, amounting to 300,000 francs, and was never actually awarded, although a satisfactory solution to the problem was ultimately discovered. In an effort to find a remedy, hundreds of suggestions were received. A catalogue of the proposals submitted, some of which were unbelievably weird, makes altogether fascinating reading.

Although the most effective answer to the problem was that of grafting *vinifera* varieties on to American rootstocks, the first effective antidote consisted of injecting carbon disulphide into the root area. This chemical certainly destroyed the bug, but the treatment was expensive; besides there was no guarantee against reinfection. The first experiment with grafting also ran into trouble, and it took some years to find suitable hybrids which could form a satisfactory union with *Vitis vinifera* and were able to flourish on European soils. As soon as the right formula had been evolved, there remained the gigantic task of replacing millions of vines all over the world.

The arrival of the phylloxera scourge had a profound effect on the French economy. Wine production in France is a major industry, and the decrease from 83 million hectolitres in 1875 to 23 million in 1889 was a disaster of unparalleled proportions. Beyond her frontiers infestation was reported to have been found in Portugal as early as 1871, in Germany and Switzerland by 1874 and in Italy by 1875. Spain was invaded in 1878, and by the following decade it had spread to Algeria. Before the turn of the century it had reached Australia and was soon to be found in South America, South Africa and New Zealand.

In spite of such relentless progress, there were certain areas which remained immune. English growers, many of whom are growing *vinifera* vines on their own roots, are hoping that the local conditions will prove too unfavourable for the insect to become established. Certainly the English climate could exercise some restraint, and this would be reinforced by the isolated nature of the vineyard. In Europe, however, it has been found that the only soils to evade contamination are those that are sandy and therefore do not allow the grubs to circulate. Clay and loam soils, for instance, are liable to contract during dry spells, allowing the insects to abandon a doomed plant and find another by surfacing through the cracks and fissures.

The life cycle of this aphis is complicated. Not only does it exist in many forms but its behaviour is irregular when associating with different members of the *Vitis* family. American vines, for instance, encourage it to exist in a form which feeds on the leaves during the summer, in addition to the usual grub that attacks the roots underground. *Vitis vinifera*, on the other hand, stimulates subterranean life and is unlikely to promote much activity on the foliage.

The insect can be identified in five different forms, all of them female except the last:

1. The fundatrix nymph, a brown grub, measuring up to 2 millimetres, which emerges from the winter egg in early spring and may be found on the leaves of the vine during the

months of May and June. Here it feeds by puncturing the upper side of the leaf and sucking the sap, at the same time injecting a poisonous saliva which causes a gall to form on the lower side. Within this gall the adult insect lays its pale yellow eggs, several hundred of them. These hatch into:

2. Gall-living insects which reproduce themselves during the summer in exactly the same way. Under favourable conditions three or four generations can be evolved producing:

3. Root-living adults, smaller insects measuring up to 1 millimetre in size and brownish in colour. By feeding on the roots these grubs create swellings and tumours, which cause irreparable damage to *vinifera* varieties but are relatively harmless to a number of American vines. Again, several generations of root-living grubs are produced before the end of the season, with some of the eggs hatching into:

4. Sexuparous insects with wings. As might be expected, these aphids escape from the soil and are able to fly a limited distance. They measure 1 millimetre in length, but their transparent wings extend beyond their bodies, which are yellow with a black thorax. They can be seen towards the end of the summer and produce eggs which can hatch into:

5. Male or female nymphs that subsequently develop into adults. The female, after mating, finds a suitable retreat in the maturer wood of the vine in order to lay a single overwintering egg. It has, however, been observed that winter eggs are very rare, or non-existent, on European *vinifera* vines. Instead the pest elects to hibernate on the roots.

It has been calculated that one overwintering egg is potentially capable of producing 4,800 million insects in a season, provided all of them survive.

Control

The only effective way of controlling this insect is to keep it out of the country. Importers of vines are supposed to inform the Ministry of Agriculture as soon as the vines come into their possession, and responsible suppliers are obliged to obtain phytosanitary certificates if they wish to sell their plants abroad. In spite of this, loop-holes exist and the English grower can only rely on the good sense of his compatriots to observe the current regulations.

Scale Insects

A family of lice belonging to a species known as *Coccidae* can sometimes be found adhering to the leaves or woody parts of a vine. Described in France as *cochenilles* and in Germany as *Schildläuse*, they consist of three main varieties: *Lecanium corni*, a small brown variety, usually observed on the fruiting canes; *pulvinaria betulae*, the woolly louse which feeds on older wood; and *phenacoccus aceris*, a pale yellow member of the family that is often to be found on the backs of leaves.

These are sucking insects, which cling to the vine and obtain their nourishment from the sap and tissues, robbing the plant of its energy and essential nutrients. In so doing they are obliged to reject part of what they consume, depositing a sticky substance on the leaves. Their tortoise-shaped shell or shield affords them some protection.

Lecanium corni, which also attacks stone fruits, appears as little brown pimples on one-year-old wood, where it takes up a permanent position as soon as it has reached maturity. The female lays around 2,000 eggs during the height of the summer which remain protected by her body until they hatch after a period of three or four weeks. The emergent larvae leave the mother and attach themselves to the underside of the leaves. In the autumn they move to the woody part of the canes or to the stem of the vine where they overwinter. In April or May of the following year they become adult and start attacking the younger wood, the leaves, the shoots and even the fruit. About half of them perish after hatching or fail to survive a severe winter. Affected vines gradually become exhausted by the persistent attention of these parasites; their vigour is impaired, and they are unable to ripen their wood.

Pulvinaria betulae is often described as the woolly variety on account of the white web it produces during the spring. It is not much bigger than *lecanium corni* but may appear so, for with its woolly throne it can easily measure more than 1 centimetre. The adult female is chestnut coloured and can lay up to 2,500 eggs which are kept protected within the web until they hatch. As soon as the larvae appear, they migrate to the leaves and shoots, where they take up residence and start to feed. By October they are mature enough to breed and overwinter on the older wood, where they prefer to hide, if possible, under the bark. The males are winged insects.

Phenacoccus aceris may be found principally in eastern France and the Rhineland. It also conceals its eggs in a web and its habits closely resemble those of *pulvinaria betulae*, from which it can be distinguished by its colour.

Control

These insects should be attacked and destroyed during the dormant period. Dinoseb or DNOC applied during the winter, paying specific attention to the stem or trunk of the vine, including the posts supporting the wire trellis, should be enough to eliminate the pests. As an alternative measure, the application of an insecticide, such as Malathion, during the summer months, would have the same result.

Spider Mites

Three types of such mites exist in Europe, two of which may be found in the northern vineyards. Red spider (*Panonychus ulmi*) and yellow spider (*Tetranychus urticae*) are prevalent in France and Germany and are able to cause considerable damage if they are not kept under control. Another yellow spider (*Eotetranychus carpini*) prefers warmer conditions and appears to be active in the South of France and Italy.

The red spider, measuring up to $\frac{1}{2}$ millimetre in length, exists in male and female form and can usually be found on the underside of a leaf. The female, larger and darker in colour, is capable of laying at least fifty eggs if conditions are favourable. The eggs are onion-shaped and, if laid in the autumn, overwinter and hatch out in the spring at the time of bud burst. They are bright red and may be found on the nodes, where the larvae will be in a strategic position to feed on the young leaves as they emerge. Two or three weeks after the eggs have hatched, the larvae will become adult insects, ready to lay eggs during the summer. This time the eggs will be laid on the underside of the leaf and coloured yellow or orange. Although the proliferation of this species will be dependent on local conditions and the microclimate, five or six generations could be propagated in a single season.

The larvae have only six legs and, if they hatch from overwintering eggs, are pale orange at first, gradually darkening to reddish-brown as they develop. Those emerging from eggs laid in the summer are yellow but soon become red as they begin to feed. The larvae change into adult insects without pupating and in doing so acquire another pair of legs.

The worst damage caused by red spider usually occurs at the time of bud burst or before any real growth has had a chance to get going. The larvae puncture the leaves and feed on the plant cells, causing large perforations to appear close to the stalk and between the veins. The debilitating effect of this treatment makes the leaves turn brown and seriously interferes with the assimilation of carbon dioxide. The leaves assume a crumpled look, and their normal development is severely retarded.

From the end of August the adult females start laying the eggs designed to survive the winter. These are deposited within the tiny cracks that appear in the bark of the older wood or else around the nodes, close to the newly formed bud. Infestations of red spider will depend for their severity on local conditions. Warm, dry weather increases their numbers; heavy manuring, especially with nitrogen, will also be favourable. The vineyards of the United Kingdom, however, are likely to be less vulnerable than those on the Continent.

The yellow spider (*Tetranychus urticae*) is, if anything, fractionally larger than the red spider, and overwinters not as an egg but as a second female. The insects take refuge either on the vine itself, concealed under the bark of the stem, or in the soil which surrounds it. In the spring, as soon as the temperature reaches 10 °C (50 °F) they begin to be active among the weeds and smaller plants in the vineyard. Unlike the red spiders, they do not attack the vines until the advent of summer. A female can lay up to 100 eggs depending on conditions, and in Europe it has been estimated that seven to ten generations will occur in a season. Periods of drought accompanied by high temperatures create favourable conditions for this insect, unlike the red spider, which tends to become less active when the thermometer registers more than 27 °C (80 °F).

Control

Attempts to exterminate the spider mites with a specific winter wash appear to have been unsuccessful so far. The best time to attack red spider appears to be soon after bud burst, when two or three leaves have emerged and the eggs are beginning to hatch. An impressive list of acaricides will provide a wide choice of spray material suitable for use against these predators: Malathion, Parathion, Metasystox, Gusathion and Tedion have all been recommended for the job. At the time of writing, Childion is said to give the best results.

Vine Weevil

One of the insect predators known to be at large in the United Kingdom belongs to a family of wingless weevils which attack rhododendrons, azaleas and camellias. The vine weevil (*Otiorrynchus sulcatus*) a member of the family, has been found to prey on cyclamen, primulas and strawberries, as well as blackberries, oaks and hazels, in addition to vines. Vineyards in Britain so far have not been seriously affected, although the pest is known to be active on the European continent.

The natural habitat of these predators may be said to exist in the woods and hedgerows of the English countryside, from which they are able to invade the private garden or greenhouse, and even stray into a vineyard. The vine weevil, which has been identified only as a female, looks like a tiny beetle, being about 1 centimetre long, and is greyish black in colour. It remains concealed in the soil during the daylight hours and ventures forth at twilight in order to feed on vine leaves and buds. The adult female can lay anything up to 500 eggs during the spring and summer; these measure about 1 millimetre in diameter, are round and white, but gradually darken as they become ready to hatch, an incubation period which lasts about three weeks. They can be found on the surface of the soil or close to the feeding roots of the vine, from which the emergent larvae will derive nourishment for the best part of a year. For the grubs are able to overwinter and do not pupate until the early spring. They appear whitish, the colour of ivory, and have a brown head. They have no legs and attain a length of 1 centimetre when fully grown. At first they nibble the finer roots of the vine, interrupting the flow of energy to the plant, but soon feed on the more substantial root system causing general debility and finally death. The pupae hatch after approximately five weeks into the adult female which immediately attacks the buds of the vine and later the young leaves. The insect causes much concern in the vineyards of Europe because it lives on the plant both above and below ground, although it is only extensive root damage that can prove fatal. Since the complete life cycle lasts a year and the adult insect can survive for three seasons, it can truly be said that the vine weevil constitutes a permanent threat. Nevertheless it is worth mentioning that these predators do not operate successfully on heavy soils which tend to impede their movement.

Control

On land where serious infestation is suspected it might be worth using carbon disulphide at the rate of 20 cubic inches per square yard as a preliminary dressing before planting takes place. In less severe cases, each vine may be planted in soil to which about half an ounce of Aldrin dust has been added. Lindane preparations and DDT dust can alternatively be sprinkled around the stem of each vine and lightly forked in. A solution made by mixing 2 pints of a 25 per cent DDT emulsion with 100 gallons of water, to which a wetter has been added, has also been found effective if watered on the roots of every vine. Europeans sometimes use Parathion but this chemical is poisonous and dangerous for bees.

Dock Sawfly

Dock sawfly (*Ametastegia glabrata*) is a troublesome pest in certain years and can usually be found where there is an abundance of dock and fat hen. Docks are familiar to most of us, and fat hen (*Chenopodium album*) are very common weeds that provide food for the caterpillars that hatch during the summer and autumn. The grub, when mature, seeks a suitable place to hibernate and by the spring has assumed the form of a chrysalis.

With the approach of winter it becomes a nuisance, especially in orchards and vineyards where it tries to find appropriate shelter from the cold. Apple trees are particularly vulnerable, for the caterpillar is inclined to burrow into the fruit itself and then decides to abandon its refuge, presumably on account of its impermanence.

The dock sawfly can lay its eggs as early as June, but a second or third generation is often produced in the later summer. The eggs are white and hatch into apple-green caterpillars, which are 1 centimetre long by the time they mature. In their search for winter quarters, they are able to penetrate the fruiting canes of vines or any other aperture to which they can easily gain access.

Control

The best way of controlling this pest would be to eliminate all types of dock from the vineyard, together with any member of the *Chenopodiaceae* family. A systemic herbicide like Roundup should be able to do this quite easily, but if the caterpillars are already there, the weeds that harbour them should be sprayed with a powerful insecticide such as Gusathion.

Wasps

The best way of keeping wasps out of the vineyard is to avoid planting grapes that ripen early. Growers who choose varieties like Siegerrebe, Ortega, Madeleine Silvaner, Précoce de Malingre or Perle de Czaba must expect to suffer losses in a bad wasp year. Vines like Müller-Thurgau ripen their fruit a little later and by that time, in England at any rate, there are not so many wasps about.

As soon as they begin to ripen, grapes attract the attention of insect predators as well as birds. Wasps, unlike bees, are able to puncture the skin of a grape; by doing so they are able to suck out the juice. Bees and fruit flies (*Drosophila melanogaster*) take advantage of the opportunity to do likewise. As a consequence, the grower is obliged to harvest his crop prematurely in order to avoid further loss.

Control

Nests are not easy to find and may be on neighbouring property, for wasps are long-range insects and are able to negotiate obstacles that defy human pursuit. An effective method of control can be provided by setting traps in April, with the object of catching queens before they have been able to raise a colony. By doing so, up to 2,500 wasps can be deprived of existence for every queen caught. Jam jars baited with redcurrant juice, to which a little vinegar and sugar has been added, can be placed in the vineyard at strategic intervals. The mouth of the jar should be covered by a transparent plastic lid which is cone-shaped and lies neatly on the rim; a small hole at the base allows the insect to enter and become trapped in the liquid. Plastic discs of this design, made to fit a 1-lb jam jar, have been on sale for such a purpose. About three traps should be sufficient for 1 acre. An alternative bait can be made by mixing 1 ounce of diammonium phosphate with 1½ pints of any fruit juice made up in the usual way from a concentrate.

10

Birds

By far the most troublesome pest to be found in the English vineyard must undoubtedly be the bird. The reasons why this is so are not difficult to determine.

As a nation we are concerned about our wild life, with the result that Britain has, to all intents and purposes, become a bird sanctuary. The only breeds that escape protection are those which are sacrificed in the name of sport and those which, like bullfinches, are officially described as pests. Blackbirds, thrushes, fieldfares and starlings are the main predators as far as vineyards are concerned but some of these are cherished songbirds which will always be protected, no matter to what extent the cultivation of vines is allowed to develop with the United Kingdom. It is therefore important to understand that these feathered thieves will remain a constant menace, which no form of legislation is ever likely to remove.

It is also important to appreciate that there is no totally effective counter-measure to the damage which birds can inflict on the generality of agricultural crops. A multitude of devices has been invented, all of which have a limited measure of success. They range from the primitive scarecrow to an elaborate network of loudspeakers, strategically placed, for the purpose of broadcasting a message of terror to the approaching marauder. However effective acoustical devices may be, it is only a matter of time before the would-be predator gets used to the disturbance and resumes its foraging activities.

Vines produce a valuable crop, so the need for effective protection becomes even more acute. In the United Kingdom vineyards are not clustered together as they are in the Médoc, the Moselle valley or the Burgenland. As a result they tend to be extremely vulnerable, becoming the sole target not only for the bird population but also for wasps. Inexperienced growers would scarcely credit the losses they are likely to suffer from concerted attacks on unprotected fruit. In all probability they would be unaware of their loss until a substantial quantity of fruit had been taken. Bunches of grapes ripen unevenly and the birds seem to be well aware of this, with the result that they remove the odd berry here and there without making much impression on the overall appearance. The grower may then be erroneously convinced that his counter-measures are pretty successful. The first indication that something is wrong may well be when he takes hydrometer readings or tests the sugar content of the juice with a refractometer. He will wonder why the Oechsle readings do not advance, unaware that the best berries are being systematically removed as they ripen.

Birds, of course, feed voraciously at dawn, when their crops are empty. Any grower prepared to undertake a dawn patrol will be thankful that grapes do not ripen along with other soft fruit, but prefer to do so when the sun rises at a more civilized hour. Nevertheless, it would be foolhardy to assume that one human presence at dawn will be effective throughout the day. Such measures, whether involving paid or unpaid labour, can be costly or wasteful nowadays.

The same objections can be used against the rearing of young sparrow hawks for vineyard protection, or even the launching of an imitation peregrine falcon suspended from a hydrogen balloon, which may, with luck, patrol a limited area for a day or two. All these ingenious measures involve somebody's time, which means they cost money.

The only effective protection so far devised seems to be the net. There are two ways of using netting and the choice will be determined by the nature and the layout of the vineyard. The vines must either be covered completely or else the area occupied by bunches of grapes will have to be effectively sealed in such a way that birds will be unable to steal the fruit.

As might be expected, the first alternative gives the best results but is often not adopted on account of the capital outlay involved. Such a decision could well be false economy, because the type of netting now being produced is so much more durable than those which have generally been available in the past. Manufacturers have discovered materials which are impervious to rain-water and, so the makers claim, unaffected by the ultraviolet rays of the sun. This means that, with reasonable care and provided cyclonic conditions do not occur, netting can be used again and again for a number of years. If, for example, the period of use can be extended over a decade, the initial cost should be divided by 10, making the annual liability of reasonable proportions, considering the value of the crop to be protected and the outlay required for alternative counter-measures.

Netting used in this way must completely envelop a section of the vineyard. It must be supported by wires secured to the top of each post, thus forming an extension of the trellis on which the vines are trained. At the extremities of each area the netting must be allowed to reach the ground and be securely attached, so that no bird can easily find a gap to breach. The wire tent pegs usually supplied by fruit-cage manufacturers are not entirely satisfactory unless enough of them are available for use. Far more effective are planks or poles laid horizontally to tether the end of the net to the ground. Provided sufficient of them are to hand, they can ensure a complete seal, which a boisterous wind will be unable to disturb. Blackbirds, one of the worst predators in the vineyard, seem to display endless patience by hopping along the edge of the netting, in the hope that a rogue wind has conveniently dishevelled the netting to a point where an easy entry can be effected. Once inside, they seem totally incapable of finding their way out, even when coaxed by the usual methods of persuasion. Expulsion therefore entails a considerable expenditure of labour and Nature seems to have endowed them with a genius for recalling their previous method of entry, so growers may find them back inside within the space of 30 minutes. As a consequence, through sheer exasperation, there might be a tendency to opt for the death penalty.

There are several types of netting on the market and some may be more acceptable than others. Lobrene, produced by Low Brothers of Dundee, is light, flexible and easy to handle, although some prefer to use Netlon. It is worth ascertaining beforehand in what sizes the netting is sold; joining strips together is a formidable task and should be avoided if the protective cover can be tailormade to fit the appropriate areas.

The type of netting used must largely depend on the layout of the vineyard. Clearly, the cost of covering an acre where the individual rows of vines are spaced at a distance of 12 feet will become prohibitive. Draping each row separately doesn't help; it uses the same quantity of netting together with a massive number of anchors to secure the extremities. In such a case it might be desirable to consider the methods used in some vineyards where the fruiting area is literally enclosed within a kind of stocking. The type of netting used, which must be imported from Germany, has the additional advantage of deterring wasps and conserving the ambient temperature from heat loss. Whether, under certain conditions, it will tend to encourage botrytis has yet to be ascertained.

11

Fungicides, Pesticides and Herbicides

The indiscriminate use of chemicals by farmers and horticulturists has recently been the subject of much criticism by those concerned with the balance of nature. The control of insect predators (for example, by the widespread application of pesticides) has been blamed for all kinds of deprivations such as the partial disappearance of our butterfly population. The careless use of hormone sprays on a windy day has often been witnessed in a flourishing vineyard by the appearance of fan leaf and the inevitable loss of fruit in the affected area. Furthermore, there is a belief that the persistent use of chemical warfare against weeds and voracious pests will eventually create an imbalance of nature by the massive build-up of poisons in the soil. Replacing the hoe with herbicides may still be regarded as a lazy kind of husbandry which should be discouraged at all costs. To spray or not to spray therefore must remain a matter for controversy.

Nevertheless, the mounting cost of labour, together with the multitude of pests and diseases that inhabit a vineyard, have forced the vigneron to invoke the aid of science when alternative measures prove uneconomic. The price of fungicides, insecticides and herbicides must also dictate a policy of caution in their use and the wisdom of restraint is a feature that surely must be taken into consideration. It is therefore wise to learn more about the lethal instruments that are available.

First of all, it must be understood that certain preparations are subject to the provisions of the Poisons Act 1972 because of the ingredients they contain. Copies of the regulations governing the labelling, storage and sale of all listed poisons can be obtained from HM Stationery Office, 49 High Holborn, London WC1V 6HB. Some products used by the agricultural community require full protective clothing, including rubber gloves, eye shield and respirator, but manufacturers are obliged to print necessary safety precautions on the label. The Ministry of Agriculture has produced a leaflet APS/1, 'The Safe Use of Poisonous Chemicals on the Farm', which can be obtained free of charge, by applying to the Ministry's Publication Department, Tolcarne Drive, Pinner, Middlesex HA5 2DT. Certain precautionary measures are worthy of note:

1. Many preparations that contain poison are lethal only in an undiluted form, so it is important to keep them stored in a suitable place and out of the reach of children. The instructions for use should be carefully observed and the recommended strength of each solution should never be exceeded. It is unwise to eat, drink or smoke when using such products. Plenty of water must be available for washing out the containers and spraying equipment. After the vines have been treated, workers should use soap to clean their hands.

2. Some care should be taken when disposing of the empty containers. In order to avoid contamination, receptacles which cannot be burned should be kept away from natural watercourses or dumps, where they might become a domestic hazard.

3. Many insecticides are poisonous to bees. It is therefore important to avoid using them when the vines are flowering for it has been established that these busy creatures find vine pollen acceptable.

4. By the same token many preparations are poisonous to fish. Great care should be taken when using these chemicals in the vicinity of water. Surplus spray material should not be allowed to find its way to a fish pond, and the disposal of empty containers should be considered in the same context.

5. Sufficient time must be allowed to elapse between the final application of a chemical spray and the harvest. Attention should be given to the maker's instructions.

6. Protection of vines involving the use of dangerous pesticides should be undertaken only by authorized persons who are physically and mentally in good health. Every care should be taken to avoid inhaling any spray likely to cause irritation to the mucous membrane and contact with exposed parts of the body should be avoided.

Any evidence of poisoning should be referred to the doctor After-effects can take the form of headache, stomach ache dizziness, sweating, trembling etc., and this may call for hospital treatment. Every effort should be made to isolate the cause o trouble and affected parts of the body should be immediately washed with soap and water. Domestic animals must, of course be treated by a veterinary surgeon.

The Application of Fungicides, Pesticides and Herbicides

English farmers and horticulturists who wish to cultivate vines successfully should adopt a programme likely to afford their vineyard the maximum protection at the minimum cost. Foreign firms such as BASF and Bayer provide charts which demonstrate the vulnerability of the vine and just how to deal with it. These may from time to time be superseded as new chemicals are discovered.

Conditions in Europe are not precisely the same as those we experience in the United Kingdom, so the spraying programme may well have to be adjusted. Broadly speaking, the British microclimate tends to encourage the development of fungous diseases and does not provide satisfactory conditions for the host of insect predators that frequent the vineyards of France and Germany. Immunity from phylloxera is an important asset, but there are other pests which could cause embarrassing losses if no measures were taken to contain them. The French list nearly a hundred species capable of inflicting damage to a vineyard; fortunately, only a handful of these are indigenous to the United Kingdom.

The routine application of fungicides and pesticides starts in the spring, soon after bud burst. Downy mildew and brenner are the first to be controlled, and then the warmer weather begins to activate the overwintering larvae and pupae of predatory insects. It is important to include a so-called 'wetting agent' in order to obtain an even distribution of the spray material and these sulphonamides must be added in the recommended strength to a container load. There are various preparations on the market such as Agral (Plant Protection) and Spreadite Liquid (Murphy); agricultural suppliers in the locality should be consulted.

The choice of a spraying machine must be undertaken with care. Considerable research has been devoted to the problem of saturating all the foliage and other parts of a plant without wasting any of the expensive spray material. It would appear that there are two types of machine on the market. The first relies on hydraulic pressure to carry the spray into the target area; the second is operated by a fan creating a current of air, which performs the same function. The efficiency of the machine is governed largely by the droplet size and the volume of spray delivered. Research has shown that better results are obtained with the use of small droplet sizes and that the same disease control can be achieved without using as much liquid. For the purposes of identification, methods of spraying can be divided into three categories: high-volume, low-volume and ultra-low-volume (ULV).

High-volume spraying means the delivery of liquid in a droplet size of more than 150 microns (0.15 mm). This will require the use of 90–350 gallons of spray per acre, depending on the amount of foliage and the number of rows. Low-volume spraying means a droplet size between 50 and 150 microns, requiring the use of 20–75 gallons of spray per acre. Ultra-low-volume spraying means a droplet size of less than 50 microns, requiring $4\frac{1}{2}$–18 gallons per acre. It must be understood that in spite of the reduction in volume, approximately the same quantity of chemical must be used, if the same measure of control is to be achieved. Theoretically, however, thanks to increased efficiency, it should be possible to make a 10–20 per cent reduction in the case of ULV applications.

Such considerations may well dispose the grower to imagine that ultra-low-volume equipment provides the ultimate solution. Unfortunately, this is not the case. ULV has been found of exceptional value in greenhouses, where the presence of wind is non-existent; in the open vineyard, however, particularly in Great Britain, the problem of drift is a very real one and could well make this type of equipment totally unsuitable.

One important problem is how to make sure that both sides of the leaves are covered with spray. This is not easy to achieve. Experiments carried out by the National Institute of Agricultural Engineering have shown that air velocities need to be between 16 and 32 feet per second if the leaves of a plant are to flutter enough to expose each surface to the spray directed against them. Clearly this must be a consideration that should be taken into account.

Inorganic Fungicides

Copper

Copper in a variety of forms has until recently been the traditional weapon used to protect the vine against the ravages of downy mildew and brenner. It has also been found effective against dead arm disease and is able to restrict the development of botrytis by toughening the texture of the grape skins. Unfortunately, copper tends to retard growth, particularly if temperatures are below normal and this could be a serious disadvantage in the United Kingdom where the season is too short as it is. Perhaps this is why the German vineyards are inclined to favour organic fungicides which, though more costly, do not interfere with the natural development of the plant. Copper sprays should never be used during the flowering period or else the fruit will fail to set; nor must they be applied during a heat wave in conjunction with wettable sulphur, for this will result in scorching. In spite of such considerations, copper is a very effective fungicide with an impressive persistence that is unlikely to be surpassed in countries where the vine has plenty of time to ripen its fruit. In the United Kingdom a case can be made for a final application of copper with the object of controlling botrytis and helping to ripen the wood.

Bordeaux Mixture

This preparation has been widely used for the control of downy mildew and, in fact, is still popular in France. It is however being abandoned in favour of organic fungicides partly on account of its incompatibility with some insecticides and partly because of its tendency to scorch the foliage, especially if it has been badly mixed. If applied during the flowering period, it is likely to cause severe coulure. The preparation of Bordeaux mixture is fairly complicated and needs to be undertaken with care. The standard method adopted on the Continent is as follows:

In order to produce 100 litres of 1 per cent strength, 1 kilogram of copper sulphate must be dissolved in 20 litres of water and 400 grams of quicklime in 80 litres of water. The copper sulphate solution must then be continuously stirred and slowly added to the limewash. On no account must the lime be added to the copper! It should then be possible to obtain a mixture that will react by turning a white phenolphthalein paper red and a red litmus paper blue. Bordeaux mixture prepared according to this formula must be used the same day as it tends to separate. However, by adding 50 grams of sugar or 1 litre of skimmed milk to 100 litres of the brew the ingredients will remain stable.

It is at the same time possible to buy various proprietary brands of copper on the market. Most of them are based on copper oxychloride and some of them are mixed with sulphur or compounds of zinc. The application rate varies with each preparation according to the strength, so it is best to follow the maker's instructions.

Wettable powder form: Cuprokylt (Universal Crop Protection), Cupravit (Bayer), Vitigran (Hoechst), Kauritil (BASF); liquid form: Fungex (Murphy).

Sulphur

The classic defence against powdery mildew. Sulphur can be applied in two ways: it can either be broadcast as a dust or else, in the form of a wettable powder, can be combined with another fungicide and sprayed over the foliage. At appropriate intervals the relevant insecticide can also be included provided a compatible chemical can be found. It is worth obtaining wettable sulphur that has been properly prepared for vineyard use, as it is important to guarantee good coverage and this can be achieved only if the particles of sulphur are sufficiently fine. In these circumstances the fungus is destroyed by absorbing the sulphur and converting it into sulphuretted hydrogen. Properly applied, wettable sulphur is effective up to a fortnight and is also useful as an acaricide. Treatment should start when the fourth or fifth leaf has appeared, and in most cases a 0.2 per cent solution should be sufficient. When conditions favour more formidable outbreaks of powdery mildew, it may be necessary to double the strength, although some care should be exercised during spells of very hot weather, when the application could cause a certain amount of scorching.

Wettable powder form: Kumulus S (BASF), Netzschwefel Bayer (Bayer), Thiovit (Sandoz).

Application: 3 lb per 100 gallons of water before flowering; 2 lb per 100 gallons of water after flowering. NB Only half-strength during spells of very hot weather.

Organic Fungicides

Benomyl

A systemic fungicide that is widely used on a variety of soft fruit, as well as on apples and various flowers. It has been found to control botrytis and powdery mildew and, when first introduced, was considered to provide a very effective solution to the dreaded *pourriture grise*. Unfortunately, this crippling fungus soon developed a strain that was able to withstand the new chemical, with the result that vinegrowers now use the preparation sparingly. It might be wise to include Benomyl in the last spray before flowering and then continue at fortnightly intervals after flowering has been completed. In addition to botrytis and powdery mildew, the chemical is effective against brenner and red spider. Benomyl is compatible with most insecticides and fungicides but should be used immediately after mixing; at least twenty-eight days must be allowed to elapse between the final application and the date of harvest. Although the fungicide is not poisonous and harmless to bees, it must be kept away from the eyes and the lungs.

Wettable powder form: Benlate fungicide (Du Pont, Dufar-Midox).

Application: 8 oz to 100 gallons of water.

Captan

A fungicide commonly used for apples and black spot in roses. For vines it helps to control downy mildew and botrytis with immediate effect. Captan is ideally suited to the maintenance of nursery beds and young vineyards. It mixes well with most spray material but is incompatible with alkaline and oil-based preparations. As a guard against two very common fungous diseases, it can prove very helpful and is fairly harmless to use. Interference with the alcoholic fermentation can be avoided if twenty-eight days are allowed to elapse between the last application and the date of harvest. Harmful to fish but not to bees.

Wettable powder form: 50 per cent Captan—Captan Fifty M & B (May & Baker), Page Captan (Page); 75 per cent Captan — Captan 83W (Stauffer), 'P.P.' Captan 83 (Plant Protection), Orthocide Concentrate (Murphy).

Application: 50 per cent Captan—2 lb to 100 gallons of water against downy mildew, 3 lb to 100 gallons of water against botrytis; 75 per cent Captan—1½ lb to 100 gallons of water against downy mildew, 2 lb to 100 gallons of water against botrytis.

Dichlofluanid

A fungicide used mainly for controlling botrytis on soft fruit. In the vineyard it has been found additionally effective against downy mildew and brenner, while discouraging oidium to some extent. It lasts longer than Captan but needs to be used at a higher concentration for the control of botrytis. Early applications are of course necessary if the vines are to be protected against brenner and peronospora. Mixes easily with wettable powders but not with some liquid insecticides. As with Captan and Benlate, the last application must be made a month before harvesting the fruit in order to avoid fermentation problems. Harmful to fish but not to bees; direct contact with the spray mist is not to be encouraged.

Wettable powder form: Elvaron (Bayer).

Application: 1½ lb to 100 gallons of water for downy mildew, 2 lb to 100 gallons of water for brenner and botrytis.

Dinocap

A fungicide used principally to control powdery mildew although fairly effective against red spider. It should be employed only after flowering has taken place, otherwise there is a danger of scorch. Incompatible with oil-based and alkaline preparations. Dangerous to fish but not to bees, it can cause irritation to the skin, eyes and respiratory system.

Wettable powder form: Karathane (Roehm & Haas).

Application: 8—12 oz to 100 gallons of water (19 per cent Dinocap)

Dinoseb (DNBP)

One of the yellow spray preparations used in Europe as a fungicide and insecticide but in the United Kingdom as a herbicide. Applied during November and December and again before bud burst in April, it will prove very effective against severe attacks of dead arm disease. It is a fairly vicious chemical, dangerous to bees, fish and livestock and also to humans if it gains access to the body; it is therefore essential to wear protective clothing and respirators when applying it.

Liquid Form: Gebutox (Hoechst).

Application: A 1 per cent solution will be sufficient to treat outbreaks of dead arm disease, provided the preparation contains 210 grams per litre Dinoseb.

DNOC (Dinitrocresol)

Another yellow spray preparation with similar qualities. Equally effective against dead arm disease and should be applied in the same way. It belongs to the same category of poisonous chemicals and should therefore be treated with the same care.

Liquid form: Sandolin A (Sandoz).

Iprodione

A new contact fungicide highly recommended for the control of botrytis. Especially useful for treating delicate foliage, such as may be found on young grafts and nursery beds. Iprodione in the form under which it is marketed is a non-hazardous fungicide which is harmless to bees and earthworms but could be dangerous to fish. It does not interfere with fermentation processes but should not be used within a week of harvest.

Wettable powder form: Rovral (May & Baker).

Application: 1¼ lb to 100 gallons (sufficient for 1 acre).

Mancozeb (Zineb–Maneb Complex)

A dithiocarbamate fungicide which suppresses downy mildew, brenner, dead arm disease and botrytis as well as controlling red spider. Satisfactory integration with wettable sulphur and most insecticides, except those containing oil or alkaline substances. Must not be used less than 28 days from the harvest. Avoid physical contact, which may cause irritation to the skin, eyes or respiratory system. Store in a dry place away from the fire. Harmless to bees.

Wettable powder form: Dithane Ultra (Hoechst).

Application: 2 lb to 100 gallons of water against downy mildew, brenner and dead arm disease; 3 lb to 100 gallons of water against botrytis.

Maneb

A dithiocarbamate fungicide for use against downy mildew, brenner and dead arm disease. Suitable for use only before

flowering. Properties generally similar to those of Mancozeb.
Wettable powder form: Maneb (BASF, Roehm & Haas).

Propineb

A dithiocarbamate fungicide for the control of downy mildew,
brenner and dead arm disease. Routine spraying with this
preparation will suppress red spider and help to reduce the
danger of botrytis. The manufacturers do not recommend it for
vines propagated on their own roots; otherwise the fungicide is
acceptable and effective without being dangerous to bees or fish.
Avoid direct contact and do not store for long periods. Mixes
easily with all but alkaline preparations. Combined with
dichlofluanid (Elvaron) it suppresses botrytis. Should not be
used within twenty-eight days of the harvest.
Wettable powder form: Antracol (Bayer).
Application: 2 lb to 100 gallons of water.

Thiram

A dithiocarbamate-type of fungicide suitable for use against
downy mildew, brenner and botrytis. The preparation is
tolerated by most plants and is quite effective against botrytis,
which it controls by direct contact. In order to avoid any
interference with the fermentation, a period of twenty-eight days
should elapse between the last spray and the harvest date.
Irritating to the skin, eyes and respiratory system but harmless to
bees. Integrates readily with other preparations. Suitable for use
in grafting operations.
Wettable powder form: BASF–TMTD–Spritzpulver (BASF),
Tripomol (Bos).
Application: 2 lb to 100 gallons of water against downy mildew
and brenner.

Vinclozolin

A new contact fungicide that effectively controls the ravages of
botrytis on flower clusters and fruit. It also reduces the risk of
stem rot and curbs the activities of red spider. It is tolerated by the
vine and can be applied at any time without ill effect except in the
case of very young growth, when it can cause some damage to the
foliage. Applied in time, it should prevent leaf botrytis as well.

Do not use within fourteen days of the harvest. Can be irritating to the skin and is harmful to fish.

Wettable powder form: Ronilan (BASF).

Application: 1 lb to 100 gallons of water.

Zineb

A dithiocarbamate fungicide that controls downy mildew, brenner and dead arm disease. Growers may not find this preparation strong enough where moist conditions prevail and should certainly supplement its application with the addition of a chemical specifically designed to combat botrytis. It is also advisable to increase the concentration of wettable sulphur for the control of powdery mildew. Can cause irritation to the eyes, skin and respiratory organs but is not harmful to bees. Harvesting can take place one week after the last application. The preparation is inflammable.

Wettable powder form: Zineb Fungicide (Plant Protection), Murphy Zineb (Murphy).

Application: 2 lb to 100 gallons of water.

Insecticides, Acaricides and Nematicides

Aldicarb

A systemic carbamate-type insecticide, acaricide and nematicide which is recommended for use in nursery beds for the control of nematodes. It should be scattered in the alleys and gently worked into the soil. This is a poisonous substance which is dangerous to fish, game and wild life; anyone affected by anticholinesterase compounds should not use this chemical. Avoid all contact.

Granular form: Temik 10 G (Union Carbide).

Application: 45 lb per acre.

Aldrin

A persistent organochlorine insecticide that is very effective for the control of vine weevil. It can also be used to eliminate wire worm, remaining active in the soil for anything up to a year. Vines are usually treated individually, about ½ oz of Aldrin being spread around the stem and lightly worked into the soil. Although the chemical is not poisonous, it should not be applied without wearing gloves. Harmful to fish but not to bees.

Powder form: Murphy Aldrin Dust (Murphy).

Azinphos–Methyl + Demeton–S–Methyl Sulphone

An organophosphorus insecticide and acaricide that is able to control a wide range of pests from cochylis and eudemis to spider mites and vine weevil. The chemical has a contact effect as well as being systemic, providing lethal nourishment in the plant upon which the insects feed. Mixes well with most chemicals, but should not be applied within three weeks of the harvest. This is a poison and should not be used by anyone affected by anticholinesterase compounds. Dangerous to bees and fish and harmful to livestock, game, wild birds and animals.

Wettable powder form: Gusathion MS (Bayer).

Application: 2 lb to 100 gallons of water.

Carbaryl

A carbamate insecticide and growth regulator used in the vineyard to control the caterpillars of the cochylis and eudemis moths. It can also be used with some effect against wasps provided it can be applied before the fruit has suffered any damage. The application needs to be repeated after ten days. It is dangerous to bees, harmful to fish and should not be used by anyone likely to be affected by anticholinesterase compounds. Avoid direct contact with the chemical and do not inhale the spray. Mixes with all but alkaline preparations. Must not be applied within two weeks of the harvest.

Wettable powder form: Sevin 85 (Union Carbide), Murvin 85 (Murphy), Midox Carbaryl 85 (Duphar-Midox).

Demeton–S–Methyl

A systemic organophosphorus insecticide and acaricide recommended for the control of red spider and other mites. It has a prompt action and persists for nearly three weeks but does not destroy the eggs. It mixes well with other chemicals but should not be used within three weeks of the harvest. It is subject to the Poisons Rules and must not be applied by anyone advised not to work with anticholinesterase compounds. Harmful to bees and fish as well as to wild birds and animals.

Liquid form: Metasystox R (Bayer).

Application: 16 fluid oz to 100 gallons of water.

Dichloropropane + Dichloropropene

An organochlorine nematicide used in the vineyards for the destruction of nematodes bearing virus diseases. Should be used in accordance with the maker's instructions. Causes severe irritation to the eyes, skin and respiratory system but is not poisonous.

Liquid form: Shell D–D Soil Fumigant (Shell).

Dichlorvos

An organophosphorus insecticide and acaride of relatively short persistence, useful in the vineyard for controlling the grubs of the cochylis and eudemis moths. Can also be effective against aphids and red spider mites. Mixes well with other chemicals provided they are not alkaline. Fairly poisonous and should be avoided by anyone affected by anticholinesterase compounds. Dangerous to bees and must not be applied within one week of the harvest.

Liquid form: Nogos 50 EC (Ciba-Geigy).

Application: 24 fluid oz to 100 gallons of water.

Dimethoate

A systemic organophosphorus insecticide and acaricide recommended for the control of red spider mites. Immediately effective on contact, it can be relied on for continuity. With the exception of alkaline material, it mixes well with most preparations and should not be applied within three weeks of the harvest. It is listed as a poison, is dangerous to bees, fish, livestock, game, wild birds and animals. It should not be used by anyone advised not to work with anticholinesterase compounds.

Liquid form: Dimethoate (Hoechst), Rogor E (Fisons), Perfektion (BASF).

Application: 16 fluid oz to 100 gallons of water.

Dinoseb (DNBP)

A contact insecticide and fungicide often used in Britain as a soil-acting herbicide. Applied during the winter, this preparation is recommended for the control of dead arm disease; used in this way it can at the same time eliminate scale insects and pupae of the tortrix moth. One application in March is sufficient unless the phomopsis infection is severe; in such circumstances earlier treatment in November or December is recommended as well. This chemical must be applied with care as it has a corrosive effect on the skin. Protective clothing should be worn and all contact with the spray must be avoided. Dangerous to fish, livestock and bees.

Liquid form: Gebutox (Hoechst).

Application: 1 gallon to 100 gallons of water for dead arm disease, $\frac{3}{4}$ gallon to 100 gallons of water for scale or tortrix moth.

DNOC (Dinitrocresol)

A contact insecticide and acaricide which, like Dinoseb, can also be used during the winter as a fungicide to control dead arm disease. It is also recommended for use against scale insects and the tortrix moth. The same precautions should be observed as with Dinoseb and the same application procedures should be adopted. Dangerous to fish, bees and livestock.

Liquid form: Sandolin A (Sandoz).

Endosulphan

An organochlorine insecticide and acaricide which effectively controls spider mites and also *Eriophyes vitis*, the gall mite, a common enough pest on the Continent but as yet unknown in this country. It should be applied as the first two or three leaves begin to unfold and should be kept well away from ponds and lakes stocked with fish. The usual precautions must be observed when using it as the Poison Rules apply. After the final spray allow thirty days to elapse before harvesting.

Liquid form: Thiodan Emulsifiable Concentrate (Hoechst).

Application: 32 fluid oz to 100 gallons of water.

Malathion

An organophosphorus insecticide and acaricide used to control eudemis, cochylis, scale insects and spider mites. Immediately effective when applied but without much persistence. Incompatible with alkaline preparations and harmful to bees and fish. The usual precautions should be taken, and no one who is affected by anticholinesterase compounds should use this chemical. Do not spray within twenty-eight days of the harvest.

Liquid form: Malathion 60 (Farm Protection), Murphy Malathion 60 (Murphy).

Application: 32 fluid oz to 100 gallons of water.

Methidathion

An organophosphorus insecticide recommended for eudemis, cochylis and spider mites. A very effective chemical with an immediate result and good persistence. It controls a number of other insects and is often used against wasps. Does not mix with alkaline preparations. This is very poisonous and should be applied with great care, all contact being avoided. Harmful to bees, livestock, game, wild birds and animals. Do not spray within twenty-eight days of the harvest.

Wettable powder form: Ultracid 40 (Ciba-Geigy).

Application: 1 lb to 100 gallons of water.

Methyl Isothiocyanate

A soil sterilant available only as a mixture with dichloropropene –dichloropropane and used for the control of virus-bearing nematodes in nursery beds. The soil is usually soaked with the preparation at least six weeks before planting and should not be allowed to come in contact with growing plants. The chemical is extremely irritating to the skin, eyes and mucous membrane.

Liquid form: DI-Trapex (PW Services).

Application: the rate of application should be according to the manufacturer's instructions.

Parathion

A contact and systemic organophosphorus insecticide and acaricide which apparently is not yet approved for use in the United Kingdom. It can be applied during the growing season and is effective against vine weevil, the tortrix moth, scale insects, spider mites, eudemis, cochylis and a number of other insect pests which may or may not exist in Britain. It can also be used against wasps. It has an immediate effect but does not persist as well as some other chemicals. It is very poisonous and should be handled with great care. Any physical contact should be dealt with immediately; affected parts should be washed with soap and water. Incompatible with alkaline products. It is harmful to bees and belongs to the top category of poisons. Two weeks should elapse between the final application and the harvest.

Liquid form: E 605 Forte (Bayer).

Application: 8 fluid oz in 100 gallons of water for scale insects, 2 fluid oz in 100 gallons of water for vine weevil, tortrix moths and spider mites.

Phosalone

An organophosphorus insecticide and acaricide recommended for use against cochylis, eudemis and spider mites. Effective for at least two weeks after application, which should take place in the early spring. Mixes well with the usual preparations but not with any that are alkaline. Although poisonous, it is not dangerous to bees if applied at the recommended strength. Allow twenty-eight days after use before harvesting the grapes. Observe the usual precautions when spraying with this material.

Wettable powder form: Rubitox (Spiess, Urania).

Application: 2 lb to 100 gallons of water.

Tetradifon

An organochlorine acaricide used principally to control the eggs and larvae of red spider mites during the summer months. It has little effect, however, on adult insects of this species, nor is it harmful to bees or insects that prey on aphids and other pests.

Liquid form: Tedion V18 (Duphar-Midox).

Tetradifon is often mixed with other chemicals and made available under a different brand name. Combined with Dicofol, an organochlorine acaricide, it is marketed as Childion and is produced by Duphar-Midox. Mixed with Carbaryl it can be obtained from BASF under the title KWP 61 and is recommended for the control of eudemis, cochylis and spider mites and tortrix moths.

Application: 1½ lb to 100 gallons of water.

Trichlorphon

An organophosphorus insecticide which is effective for the control of tortrix moths. It is also used on the Continent for cochylis and eudemis. The action is immediate and the persistence satisfactory. Incompatible with alkaline preparations and harmful to fish and bees. Not recommended for anyone allergic to anticholinesterase compounds and must not be applied within ten days of the harvest.

Wettable powder form: Dipterex SL (Bayer).

Application: 1½ lb to 100 gallons of water.

Herbicides

Aminotriazole

A translocated or systemic herbicide. Often used in conjunction with Simazine for the control of annual and perennial weeds. Absorbed by the leaves, it interferes with the formation of chlorophyll and is able to penetrate down to the roots. Combined with Simazine, it remains effective for six months and should be applied when the weeds are 4 or 5 inches high. Contact with the eyes, skin and respiratory organs should be avoided. Harmless to bees.

Wettable powder form (Simazine and Aminotriazole): Domatol (Ciba-Geigy).

Application: 5 lb to 100 gallons of water (sufficient for 1 acre).

Chlorthiamid

A soil-acting herbicide available in granular form which is ideal for spot treatment of awkward weeds such as couch, thistle or bindweed, especially where these are found growing close to a vine. The preparation can be applied manually and needs moisture to release its potency into the soil. It attacks the cell tissues and interferes with the germination and growth of seeds. Results are noticeable after two weeks, when the weeds begin to look decidedly anaemic. The herbicide should never be used in a newly planted vineyard; treatment should be delayed until the third or fourth growing year. Application is usually made in the spring during March, April or May, before the ground becomes too dry. Avoid direct contact when applying; fairly harmful to bees.

Granular form: Prefix (Shell).

Application: Approximately ½ cwt per acre. For deep-rooted and difficult weeds double this rate.

Dichlobenil

Another soil-acting herbicide with similar properties. A little less soluble than Chlorthiamid and unlikely to penetrate the top soil by more than 6 inches. Rather more dangerous to bees and should be used only in established vineyards.

Granular form: Casoron G (Duphar-Midox, BASF, Bayer).

Application: Similar to Chlorthiamid.

Diquat

A contact herbicide widely used to clear annual weeds from the vineyard. It has a corrosive action and any foliage upon which it falls is almost immediately burned. It is invaluable for treating weeds that persist in growing beneath the wire trellis-work upon which the vines are supported. Although it is customary to use it during the dormant period, it can also be applied in the summer, provided the danger of drift can be prevented by fitting a protective hood and directing the spray directly on to the ground. Diquat is absorbed by the leaves and results are apparent almost at once, although applications must be repeated from time to time, as the corrosive action affects only the foliage with which it comes in contact. It can be used to eliminate weeds from a seed bed before sowing or to clean an area intended for green manuring. It is supposed to leave no harmful residues in the soil, but contact with eyes and skin should be avoided, and the spray must not be inhaled. Harmful to animals but not to bees.

Liquid form: Reglone (Celamerck, Plant Protection).

Application: 1 pint to 25–50 gallons of water.

Glyphosate

A translocated herbicide which, when absorbed by the leaves, circulates within the plant and destroys it. A period of several days will elapse before the desired effect becomes apparent. The preparation is excellent for the spot treatment of difficult weeds such as couch grass, ground alder and bindweed but must be used with great care in order to avoid drift. Treatment is to be recommended only during the vegetative period, when the weeds are actively growing. Control should be exercised when operating near water, as the herbicide is harmful to fish.

Liquid form: Roundup (Monsanto).

Application: 2 pints to 100 gallons of water (sufficient for 1 acre).

Linuron

A soil-acting herbicide derived from urea which can be used either alone or in combination with other weedkillers. When first applied, it appears to have no effect but should produce results within one or two weeks. Care should be taken to avoid contact with the eyes or skin; some irritation will be caused if the vapour is inhaled. The herbicide is best applied in the spring, when conditions are moist and the weeds show about 1 inch of growth.

Wettable powder form: Afalon (Hoechst). Also available in liquid form.

Application: 5 lb to 100 gallons of water.

MCPA

A translocated herbicide belonging to a group described as growth regulators or hormone weedkillers. These preparations must be used with great care in a vineyard, for the foliage is extremely sensitive to any direct contact. They should never be used at flowering time and every effort should be made to avoid drift. Perhaps the safest time to use hormone sprays is after flowering, when the growth has become less vigorous. Very effective results can be obtained by treating bindweed and thistle, both troublesome weeds to find in a vineyard. Spraying equipment should be carefully cleaned after use because these herbicides can cause damage at very low concentrations. Although harmless to bees and not poisonous, some care should be taken to avoid direct contact with this chemical. Diabetics are advised not to use it. MCPA is available in liquid or powder form at various concentrations. Application rates should be according to the manufacturer's instructions.

Mecoprop (MCPP)

Another translocated herbicide belonging to the same category of hormone weedkillers. Very effective against many difficult plants such as thistle and bindweed but dangerous to use in a vineyard unless adequate care has been taken to avoid drift. The same precautions should be taken as with MCPA, and diabetics might do better to choose another herbicide. Mecoprop is also available in liquid or powder form at various concentrations; the rate of application should be according to the manufacturer's instructions.

Paraquat

A contact herbicide belonging to the same group as Diquat, exhibiting the same corrosive action when applied and generally used for the same purposes. Growers often mix the two chemicals together and repeat the applications when these become necessary. Paraquat contains active ingredients scheduled as poisons and is harmful to animals but not to bees.

Liquid form: Gramoxone (Plant Protection).

Application: 1 pint to 25–50 gallons of water.

Simazine

A soil-acting herbicide that is often included in mixtures with others. It is used mainly in the vineyard to prevent the germination of seeds but can also arrest the development of those that have already germinated. This it can do by interrupting the action of photosynthesis, with the result that they die within a week. Although Simazine is active for the best part of six months, it depends on the presence of moisture and is unable to function during a period of drought. With its sphere of influence confined to the top soil, it is ineffectual against deep-rooted weeds and should be applied in the early spring, when the ground is still wet. Contact with the chemical should be avoided; eyes, skin and the respiratory organs are vulnerable. Harmless to bees.

Wettable powder form: Gesatop 50 WP (Ciba-Geigy), BH Simazine 50 WP (Diamond Shamrock). Also available in liquid form: Murphy Simazine SC (Murphy).

Application: 1 lb to 40 gallons of water.

A Suggested Spraying Programme for English Vineyards

Application rate according to maker's instructions.

Time of application	Materials	Purpose
November	Paraquat (Gramoxone) or Diquat (Reglone)	Removal of weed growth
November/December and if necessary again in February/March	DNOC (Sandolin) or Dinoseb (Gebutox) or Tar Oil (Mortegg Emulsion)	Dead arm disease

Time of application	Materials	Purpose
March	Simazine (Gesatop)	Elimination of weed seeds
April (large woolly bud)	Captan (Orthocide Concentrate)	Dead arm disease
May (leaves about 1 inch in diameter)	Mancozeb (Dithane) together with Demeton–S–Methyl (Metasystox) and a sulphonamide	Downy mildew and various predatory insects
May/June (2–3 weeks later)	Mancozeb, together with wettable sulphur and a sulphonamide	Downy mildew and powdery mildew
June (2–3 weeks later)	Mancozeb, together with wettable sulphur and a sulphonamide	Downy mildew and powdery mildew
July (2–3 weeks later)	Mancozeb, wettable sulphur, Vinclozolin (Ronilan) and a sulphonamide	Downy mildew, powdery mildew and botrytis

Flowering period—Avoid spraying if possible (but not by more than 14 days if weather is unfavourable)

Time of application	Materials	Purpose
July (2–3 weeks later)	Mancozeb, wettable sulphur, Vinclozolin and a sulphonamide	Downy mildew, powdery mildew and botrytis
August (2–3 weeks later)	Mancozeb, wettable sulphur, Vinclozolin and a sulphonamide	Downy mildew, powdery mildew and botrytis
August/September (2–3 weeks later)	Mancozeb, wettable sulphur, Vinclozolin and a sulphonamide	Downy mildew, powdery mildew and botrytis
September	Vinclozolin	Botrytis

The most important anti-botrytis spray is that which immediately follows flowering.

Mancozeb (Dithane) may be replaced by Propineb (Antracol), Thiram, Zineb or other preparations considered effective against downy mildew.

Wettable Sulphur may be replaced by Dinocap (Karathane) for use against powdery mildew.

Vinclozolin (Ronilan) may be replaced by Iprodione (Rovral) for use against botrytis.

Demeton-S-Methyl (Metasystox) may be replaced by whatever insecticide proves to be most effective against a difficult pest.

12

Vine Varieties

Before deciding what varieties to plant, the grower should make up his mind what kind of wine he would like to produce and what sort of vineyard he wants to establish. Thanks to our hazardous climate, the range of cultivars is somewhat limited, so it is worthwhile considering the nature of each variety before coming to any conclusion. Growers for instance must decide whether they want their vineyard to pay its way or whether they will be prepared to keep it going for fun. A preference for red wine, for example, and a determination to produce it, may not be the best way to make an English vineyard profitable.

The varieties mentioned in this book are not simply confined to those that are able to ripen in this country. The list also contains some that require better conditions than they are likely to get in southern England; they are included partly on account of their reputation but principally because they have already been planted experimentally in a number of vineyards. Lack of space prevents the inclusion of other varieties such as Madeleine Silvaner or Kanzler that are quite capable of ripening their fruit in Great Britain.

The following pages, giving the main characteristics of each vine, are intended to serve as a guide to the grower. The origin of the species, together with such features as the vulnerability to fungous disease, a recommended rootstock, an estimated harvest yield and the potential specific gravity of the must are given where appropriate. Must weights (approximate sugar content) are given as degrees Oechsle, which represent the last two figures recorded by an ordinary hydrometer (thus 1060 becomes 60°Oechsle).

Auxerrois

Auxerrois has significance for the English grower because the EEC elected to choose it as one of the recommended varieties for cultivation in the United Kingdom. This may appear odd, since it has the reputation for ripening its fruit rather late, possibly too late for a satisfactory performance in our difficult climate. In spite of this, the variety is popular in Luxemburg and may, with clonal selection, do equally well in this country.

The vine, which is sometimes known as Auxerrois Blanc de Laquenexy, can also be found in Alsace, Champagne and Burgundy, as well as in Baden, the Upper Moselle and other parts of Germany. As a prospect for England it is unlikely to appeal, for the yield is not brilliant, rarely exceeding 3½ tons per acre. It needs a first-class site, well protected from the wind, because the flowers will fail to set if they are exposed to bad weather. Although not over-sensitive to fungous diseases, the variety may develop berry botrytis if subjected to intensive planting, it is therefore better to allow adequate spacing between the rows and plants and, if necessary, to remove excessive foliage. SO4 is the recommended rootstock, although 5C can be used instead; on poorer soil it might be worth substituting 125AA. Given reasonable fertility, the Auxerrois is a vigorous grower, ripening the new wood so effectively that it stands up to the winter frosts better than many varieties.

The must, if properly ripe, should show an Oechsle weight of 80° or more, with an acidity of 0.6–0.8 per cent. The wine is rather neutral but full-bodied, with a fairly substantial bouquet. Small quantities have been produced in England with notable results. English growers who are able to ripen the fruit of this variety should plant special clones in order to improve the yield.

Bacchus

The new cultivar Bacchus, a product of the Research Institute at Geilweilerhof in the Palatinate, is very promising and, as a result, has been planted in many wine-producing districts of Germany. Thanks to the brisk demand, the plant is not easy to import, although it has managed to find its way into a few English vineyards. A splendid variety by all accounts, giving a huge yield of grapes under suitable conditions; it may be a little late for the United Kingdom.

Given the right site and a good depth of rich soil, it is a variety which should certainly be cultivated in this country. It is very vigorous and must therefore be given sufficient room. Allow not

less than 4 feet 6 inches between the vines and 5–6 feet between the
rows. Closer spacing might well encourage stem rot and botrytis,
particularly in years of prolific yield. The variety is likely to derive
some benefit from careful defoliation at the right time of year.

The best rootstocks are SO4 and 5C unless the soil lacks
fertility, when it might be better to use 5BB or 125AA. Not more
than ten buds per square yard should be retained after pruning.
The canes have the reputation of ripening well, so the variety is
unlikely to suffer from winter frosts.

The harvest, which takes place a little later than that of Müller-
Thurgau, can yield as much as 8 tons per acre. Although it is
claimed that quality is not impaired by such bounty, the Institute
recommends a restricted yield of 6–7 tons per acre, in order to
maintain the high standards with which the wine is associated. It is
certainly true to say that in spite of these high yields an average of
77 °Oechsle seems to be achieved in the Palatinate. The wine has a
flowery bouquet, plenty of extract and a fruity muscat flavour.

The variety was obtained by crossing a Silvaner × Riesling with
Müller-Thurgau.

Blaue Zweigelt Rebe

The Blaue Zweigelt Rebe is one of the few vines from which the
English ought to find it possible to make a satisfactory red or rosé
wine. It is a true *Vitis vinifera*, produced in Austria by crossing
Blaufränkisch with St Laurent. It first saw the light of day during
the Second World War and was bred by Dr Fritz Zweigelt, a
Director of the Hohere Bundeslehranstalt für Wein- und Obstbau
at Klosterneuburg near Vienna. Dr Zweigelt was a very good
friend of Professor Dr Lenz Moser, who was one of the first to test
the new variety in his own experimental station at Rohrendorf. It
was Moser himself who suggested that the new cultivar should
be named after the breeder, and the title 'Blaue Zweigelt Rebe'
has now been officially recognized.

The English grower will find this variety worth planting mainly
because its fruit ripens quite early in the season. It is earlier than
Pinot Noir, for example; this gives it a better chance of maturing
its wood and resisting low temperatures during the winter.
Eighteen degrees of frost (0 °F) can be tolerated, provided the
wood has ripened properly. This does not mean to say that Blaue
Zweigelt Rebe can be planted in a frost pocket; like many others,

the variety is vulnerable to low temperatures in the autumn and spring.

Yields in Austria average around 4 tons per acre, although as much as 7 or 8 tons can be produced in a good year. Owing to the vigour of its growth, Blaue Zweigelt Rebe is well adapted to high-culture systems and others that require wide spacing, so plenty of room should be allowed between the rows. In areas where the average temperature for the year reaches 9°C (48°F), an Oechsle reading of over 75° should be achieved, with acidities of 0.65–0.9 per cent.

Chardonnay

A vine that needs no introduction, as it is responsible for producing some of the most famous white wines in the world. Names like Montrachet, Meursault, Chablis and Pouilly-Fuissé are part of the heritage for which France is famous, without mentioning the Côte des Blancs in Champagne. The Chardonnay vine is also grown in other parts of France, notably Alsace, and can be found in Germany, Austria and Switzerland. In some countries it is known as Weisser Klevner or Weisser Burgunder, but nowhere has its wine reached the same degree of perfection as that which is produced in France. Some confusion has existed as to whether all the synonyms refer to the same vine variety; names such as Pinot Blanc, Auvernat, Morillon Blanc, etc., have been used in different localities, to say nothing of the unfamiliar titles that may be found in Eastern Europe.

It is very natural, of course, that English growers should be anxious to try to grow this famous vine on their side of the Channel, and with customary enthusiasm a few have devoted sections of their vineyards to this noble plant; as one grower remarked, 'pour ajouter un peu de noblesse'. Chardonnay must, however, be ranked with Pinot Noir, Kerner and Schönburger: rather too late for our climate and scarcely worth planting, unless the vineyard is in a position favourable enough to guarantee an Oechsle weight of 80°. Bud burst occurs after Pinot Noir, and the fruit ripens later, but after a good summer it might prove satisfactory on an exceptional site.

The variety is not over-sensitive to fungous diseases and is able to withstand botrytis, stem rot and stem atrophy better than most. Not only will it be necessary to choose a favourable site for

Chardonnay, but the nature of the soil will also have to be suitable. This should be fertile and moisture retentive, with plenty of depth. Poor, shallow soils are not recommended, although some degree of compensation can be effected by using a vigorous rootstock such as 5BB or 125AA. On rich ground SO4 or 5C would be the best choice.

Growth is fairly vigorous, and the wood ripens well enough to protect the plant against extremes of temperature during the winter; on the Continent it could suffer damage from May frosts, but this is unlikely to happen in the United Kingdom. The vine should be given plenty of room and will benefit from wide spacing. On no account should the rows be closer than 5 feet 6 inches apart, and there should be nearly the same distance between the vines. Closer spacing will encourage the plant to suffer coulure, particularly when the weather is unfavourable at flowering time. Some of the high-culture—Pendelbogen, for instance—systems might suit the variety well, for growers have experienced the best results by retaining two long, well-arched fruiting canes.

French and German textbooks insist that a good must weight is essential if the vine is to be considered worth growing. Oechsles under 80° tend to produce disappointing wines, and if better results cannot be obtained, the vigneron would do better to choose another variety. Acidity is usually fairly high and is likely to be more than 1 per cent. The yield per acre varies from 1 to 6 tons, with a Continental average of $4\frac{3}{4}$ tons. As in the case of Pinot Noir, much will depend on the type of clone planted.

Faber

Georg Scheu produced this new cultivar in 1929 by crossing Weisser Burgunder with Müller-Thurgau. The vine has much to commend it and should be planted more widely in Britain, for it makes a wine of breeding and traditional flavour. It is often to be found in areas where Riesling cannot ripen, since it tends to be ready for harvesting a week before Müller-Thurgau. The yield is also satisfactory if the vine can be made to hold its bunches, for it seldom suffers from coulure; in Germany it averages more than 5 tons per acre.

Faber is not particular about soil and not especially susceptible to fungous diseases, but it has the reputation of allowing its bunches to fall on the ground as a result of stem atrophy. Whether this is due to local conditions is something the grower would be well advised to find out, by planting a row as an experiment, before committing the entire vineyard to such a variety.

Experience has shown that a vigorous rootstock like 125AA will suit this vine best. Thanks to its rather weak growth, that or Kober 5BB should be chosen; SO4 will be suitable only on very fertile soils.

The variety ripens its wood very well and therefore stands up to low temperatures during the winter. The most suitable method of training is probably Single Guyot, with the plants spaced at distances of 4 feet and the rows 5 feet apart. Faber should give a higher Oechsle reading than Müller-Thurgau and should contain slightly more acid, but much will depend on the date of harvest, for the fruit can with advantage be left on the vine until after that of Müller-Thurgau has been gathered. In Germany Faber is often used for Spätlese.

Gutenborner

Gutenborner is a new Geisenheim cultivar that is gaining support in the United Kingdom. It was produced by crossing Müller-Thurgau with Chasselas. It is a variety which is unlikely to do well on every site, so it may not be ideal for cultivation in this country. It needs good friable soil and is inclined to suffer from fungous diseases. For that reason it should be given plenty of space and is likely to respond to the Pendelbogen method of training.

Its vigorous growth should be curbed by a moderate rootstock such as 5C or SO4. For high-culture systems, such as Lenz Moser and Geneva Double Curtain, Kober 5BB is to be recommended.

The harvest, which should take place after that of Müller-Thurgau, could yield as much as 5 tons per acre and give a must weight of up to 85 °Oechsle. Acidity may range from 1 to 1.5 per cent expressed as tartaric. The wine is distinguished, somewhat reminiscent of a Riesling, although perhaps more neutral in flavour. In England the vine should be planted only on a good site, preferably frost-free.

Huxelrebe

This new cultivar is a cross between Chasselas (Gutedel or Fendant) and Courtillier Musque, which was produced by Georg Scheu in 1927, at the Alzey Research Institute. It takes its name from a grower called Fritz Huxel, who first recognized its potential qualities and understood how to handle it. It has been planted with success in some English vineyards but is clearly not suited to every site.

The variety is distinguished by its large leaves and abundant display of fruit, the berries reaching a size not normally associated with wine grapes. Growth is extremely vigorous, with a yield tending to be far too generous and therefore damaging to the plant. Some restraint must therefore be exercised, by removing flower trusses rather than by hard pruning.

Huxelrebe does not care for chalk or soils with a binding texture; it flourishes on well aerated ground and should therefore respond to generous applications of humus. It needs protection from the wind and cannot thrive on poor soil. Bad weather at flowering time causes millerandage, substantially reducing the weight of its large bunches. Potential fruiting canes do not ripen all that well and the variety suffers rather easily from botrytis.

As a consequence, it benefits from generous spacing and should be planted in rows not less than 5 feet 6 inches apart with 4 feet 6 inches between the vines themselves. The main stem should measure not less than 2 feet 3 inches, with two fruiting canes arched over a supporting wire. Six to eight buds per square yard are generally recommended. In order to support its growth a vigorous rootstock is necessary; the variety is usually grafted on to 5C, but in fertile soils it may do better on 5BB or 125AA.

The fruit ripens early and may attract wasps. It is generally harvested a week earlier than Müller-Thurgau and often records a higher specific gravity. If picking can be delayed, the variety can produce a wine of exceptional quality, with sufficient acidity and plenty of extract. In spite of this, the powerful muscat bouquet and flavour do not appeal to everybody, although some find its character much to their taste.

Kerner

Kerner is a variety that everyone would like to grow, principally because of the wine that can be made from its fruit. This is of exceptional breeding, similar to wines made from the Riesling grape but with a muscat bouquet of some delicacy. Unfortunately, it is really too late for England unless a very warm, sheltered spot can be found. A new cultivar, registered in 1969, Kerner was produced at the Weinsberg Research Institute by crossing Trollinger (Black Hamburg) with Riesling. It is becoming increasingly popular in Germany, not only thanks to the wine it produces but also on account of its frost resistance in the winter.

Kerner tends to grow plenty of side shoots and therefore too much foliage, so any intensive culture should be avoided. If the vines are close together, botrytis will attack the fruit; it therefore pays to keep the plants at least 5 feet apart with 6 feet between the rows. The stem or trunk of the vine should measure not less than 2 feet 6 inches, and the arched canes of adjacent plants should have a clearance of 4 inches between them. Pendelbogen should suit this variety well, with a vigorous rootstock such as 125AA or 5BB. Apart from botrytis, Kerner is unlikely to be troubled by fungous diseases and will grow well on most soils. It ripens its wood well and, under the best conditions, can produce up to 6 tons per acre. The must should register slightly more sugar than Müller-Thurgau if it can be made to ripen, with an acidity of about 1 per cent. Provided botrytis can be kept at bay, it pays to defer the harvest as long as possible, since the plant is fairly frost resistant and should continue to ripen its fruit.

Madeleine Angevine

A *vinifera* variety originally produced in the middle of the nineteenth century, which has found favour in England in spite of a habitual reluctance to set its fruit. It was obtained by crossing the French cultivars Précoce de Malingre with Madeleine Royale. The breeding took place at Angers near the river Loire—hence the name.

The tendency to coulure can to some extent be offset by cultivation close to other varieties. This improves the pollination of the female flowers, which often appear in some abundance. The fruit ripens reasonably early, except in cold summers, and should be harvested by the middle of September; not as early as Madeleine Silvaner or Madeleine Céline, which do not produce as vigorous growth. Madeleine Angevine, on the other hand, can be adapted to high-culture systems, although it is usually trained to rather long, well arched fruiting canes on Double Guyot.

The fruit is greenish-yellow, on longish stalks, and the wine should produce a delicate muscat flavour with a good bouquet. It is easy to grow and not very particular about soil but should never be planted on cold sites, because of the rather disappointing yield that may occur after so much early promise.

Some English growers have had considerable success with this variety, and, given the right conditions, it could prove to be a good all-purpose vine for this country. Care should be taken with the vinification, however, in order to avoid a mediocre result. Perhaps the best reason for growing Madeleine Angevine would be to use the must for blending with that of another suitable variety.

Similar in many respects, although very neglected in the United Kingdom, is the parent vine Madeleine Royale, another French cultivar also produced at Angers. Ray Barrington Brock strongly recommended this variety as a consequence of his painstaking research work during the 1950s.

Müller-Thurgau

Known in some countries as Riesling Silvaner, a title which has been abbreviated in Luxemburg to 'Rivaner', this variety was produced in 1882 by Dr Müller, who came from a canton in Switzerland called Thurgau. At the time he was working as an assistant at the famous German Research Institute at Geisenheim. At the Swiss Institute of Wädenswil, where he returned in 1891, the new cultivar was carefully nurtured and released for commercial use. Few could have foreseen its future potential.

The EEC, in an attempt to rationalize, has outlawed the name Riesling Silvaner as being a meaningless description; the Riesling and Silvaner vines have been crossed again and again, so the name has absolutely no significance. Added to which, there has been some speculation about the true origin of this famous variety; it appears that the plant shows all the characteristics of a Riesling–Riesling cross, and it has been suggested that an error has crept into the records. Be that as it may, the EEC has permitted the abbreviation 'Rivaner' as a description for the variety because the Luxemburgers adopted it more than fifty years ago.

The new cultivar made little progress at first. Although it returned to Germany in 1913, it was not until after the First World War that it began to attract attention. It is fascinating to follow its steady growth of popularity and to observe that in Germany at least it has quite recently become the most widely planted variety. Müller-Thurgau came to the United Kingdom with a peerless reputation but has suffered criticism from growers who have planted it and been disappointed with results. Whether the criticism is justified remains to be seen; only time will decide whether this vine will become as popular here as it has in Germany.

Perhaps the variety needs a warmer summer than Britain can provide in order to maintain the handsome yield obtained in other parts of Europe. For Müller-Thurgau does not easily ripen its wood. A wet autumn with ideal conditions for botrytis, a disease from which the variety is prone to suffer, prevents the canes from maturing properly and providing adequate fruit buds for the following season. The abundant harvest which English growers enjoyed in 1976 was due mainly to a fine spell of weather that occurred during the months of July and August 1975.

Müller-Thurgau can easily fall a victim to the ravages of downy mildew and botrytis. Anyone growing the vine in Britain should watch out for these dangerous fungous diseases, particularly when the climate is hostile. Dead arm disease can also occur, although powdery mildew can be less of a menace. Every attempt should be made to maintain a regular spraying programme, stepping up the frequency of applications if conditions determine.

For the same reason Müller-Thurgau vines should never be planted too close together; it is important to guarantee a good circulation of air in the vineyard. Growers are therefore recommended to allow at least 6 feet between the rows and 4 feet 6 inches between the vines. The fruiting canes must never be allowed to overlap; indeed it is better to allow a gap of several inches, so that any likelihood of crowding will be avoided.

The Müller-Thurgau vine is not really fussy about soil or site, although it prefers fertile conditions with an adequate supply of moisture; sandy, gravelly soils are less suitable, and it seems to be unhappy when planted on chalk. Its ability to yield a massive harvest when conditions are favourable is an indication that it requires feeding more generously than other varieties. English vineyards tend to be more fertile than those on the Continent but should not be starved as a consequence. Yields of 6 tons per acre are not impossible in Britain (several growers experienced this in

1976), and in Germany the variety is capable of producing half as much again without causing excessive damage to the plant. It stands to reason therefore that stocks of nutrients should be replenished, and above all the levels of potassium and magnesium need to be carefully checked. Nitrogen should be applied in small doses when necessary, if possible during the spring rather than in the autumn.

Susceptibility to many of the fungous diseases means that Müller-Thurgau must be given more room in the vineyard. Intensive cultivation with a traditional spacing of 5 feet by 4 feet is really too close for the United Kingdom; at least 6 feet should be allowed between the rows, preferably between 6 feet 6 inches and 7 feet. With spacing 4 feet between the plants would be feasible, but again 4 feet 3 inches or 4 feet 6 inches would be better. Thanks to its vigour, it should be possible to obtain a comparable yield by allowing up to a dozen fruiting buds on each cane. The Pendelbogen method of training is now being adopted for Müller-Thurgau, and care is taken to allow at least 1 foot of daylight between the adjacent fruiting canes.

The variety is inclined to be irregular in growth. This, coupled with a reluctance to ripen its wood, induces the vigneron to consider adopting a system that preserves four short fruiting canes or extended spurs. Such a method might be compared with the Lenz Moser high-culture system, with the main cordon trained horizontally at a distance of 4 feet from the ground.

Müller-Thurgau ripens early and, if caught by the frost, has additional buds which are capable of producing a somewhat reduced crop, provided conditions are favourable. In a good year most English vineyards will harvest the grapes in October, although a poor summer and late flowering are likely to delay the event until the following month.

It is a mistake to choose anything but vigorous rootstock for Müller-Thurgau. On fertile ground where the variety does well it is certainly better to use SO4 or 5C, but if the soil does not encourage strong growth, Kober 5BB or 125AA are to be preferred. Immunity from phylloxera means that ungrafted vines may also be planted in Britain, and reports suggest that these have done better in many cases.

Müller-Thurgau, when ripe, achieves an Oechsle reading of 70° to 75°, but in England growers may have to be content with a lower figure, especially when the yield of fruit is substantial. Furthermore, the must has an acidity which should not be allowed to become too low; indeed, the level of acidity may well determine the date of the harvest and therefore the Oechsle reading—that is, provided the incidence of botrytis has not fixed it already.

Thanks to their vigorous growth and abundant foliage, Müller-Thurgau vines must be controlled by carefully removing sterile shoots and fading leaves in the fruiting area; such action, taken before the harvest, will increase the circulation of air and help to reduce the premature onset of botrytis.

The wine, when made from fully ripe fruit, acquires an attractive muscat flavour and a pleasing bouquet. At its best it can show quite remarkable quality. Many people prefer to drink it while it is still young and fruity; certainly, as a general rule it is not a wine to keep more than two years.

Ortega

Produced at the Bavarian Institute in Veitshöchheim (Würzburg) by crossing Müller-Thurgau with Siegerrebe, the variety is named after the Spanish philosopher José Ortega y Gasset.

It ripens early in the year and is therefore extremely vulnerable to wasp damage; it should be planted in a sheltered position because it simply hates cold wind, particularly at flowering time. Although it resists low temperatures during the winter, bud burst is early enough to expose it to May frosts. Unlike some vines that require 100 days to ripen their fruit after flowering, Ortega should manage to achieve the same result in eleven or twelve weeks.

The variety is not particular about soil or site, provided there is adequate protection from the wind. Growers who choose Ortega as their main crop should plant this vine only on a sheltered site if they want to guarantee a consistent harvest. SO4 is the best rootstock.

In general, the variety is a good one, not particularly susceptible to fungous diseases, with a satisfactory yield and a reputation for producing first-class wines. Potential fruiting canes mature well, so there should be no lack of fruit buds for the following year.

The vine is likely to have many leaves and should therefore be given plenty of space. At least 5 feet should be allowed between the plants, with possibly more between the rows. The stem should be allowed to measure about 2 feet, and twelve fruiting buds per square yard must be left after pruning. The variety ripens its grapes earlier than Müller-Thurgau and can yield up to 5 tons per acre on a protected site. Must weights are often high, sometimes reaching more than 90°Oechsle, with an acidity that will rarely require adjustment.

Ortega can produce a wine of outstanding quality with a bouquet reminiscent of peaches. It should be bottled at an early date and needs a fair time to mature.

Pinot Gris

A vine that originated in Burgundy, Pinot Gris has been cultivated in Europe for centuries. Understood to be related to Pinot Noir, it has now been established in many countries and represents one of the more important varieties of West Germany, where it is popularly described as Ruländer, having been introduced by a certain Johann Ruland of Speyer. In Alsace the vine is also known as Tokay, although this title has nothing whatever to do with the famous wine of Hungary made from Furmint grapes.

Pinot Gris has been planted in some English vineyards but does not appear to have been entirely successful. This may be due to late ripening. In order to get the best results from this variety, it is important to obtain a high specific gravity in the must, which could be difficult in our cold climate. If the Oechsle reading is less than 70°, the wine tends to be unsatisfactory; to produce a decent wine the must weight should be at least 10° higher.

If it is to be successful in England, Pinot Gris must have a really good site. Like Riesling, it will need every possible advantage in order to ripen its fruit in the limited English season. It needs plenty of rich, warm top soil and cannot flourish on poor ground containing gravel or sand. Relatively wide spacing is also important, for the variety is fairly vigorous, requiring two long fruiting canes, which should be well arched over supporting wires. Vines should be planted 5 feet apart, with at least 5 feet 6 inches between the rows. If Pinot Gris is cordon-trained, a treatment to which it is well suited, the plants should be spaced at a distance of 6 feet 6 inches. In fact, this variety responds to most of the high-training methods and should be tried out with the Pendelbogen system in Britain.

Pinot Gris ripens its wood efficiently and stands up well to low temperatures. It is also resistant to fungous disease, including botrytis, although the grapes have a way of forming tight bunches as a result of sound pollination at flowering time. Stem rot and stem atrophy should cause no problems, and the yield per acre could be as much as 5 tons. In the United Kingdom the best rootstocks would probably be SO4 or 5C; on clay soils 26G could also be used.

Given the right conditions, Pinot Gris can produce first-class wine with a high extract and plenty of character. Whether our English climate will be able to provide such conditions will be revealed in the fullness of time.

Pinot Meunier

Not long ago some interest was aroused by the performance of a vine growing in Kent, which was later identified as Pinot Meunier, a variety which may have originated in Burgundy as a mutation of Pinot Noir. The vine was found in the village of Wrotham and considered to have been there for at least two hundred years. After that period of time, it was agreed, the plant should have adapted itself to the idiosyncrasies of the British climate. It was given a fair trial in the Beaulieu vineyard and contributed to the production of a rosé wine. Its performance was adequate but hardly good enough, for it was later grubbed in favour of other varieties.

It was perhaps the Beaulieu venture that inspired the EEC to include it among the varieties recommended for the United Kingdom. Wrotham Pinot, as it came to be called, was a synonym permitted by the Community, presumably out of deference to its doubtful origin, and must therefore take its place alongside Müllerrebe and Schwarzriesling. The variety is sometimes referred to as Dusty Miller on account of the new growth, which has the appearance of being covered with white flour.

Pinot Meunier is to be found not only in Burgundy but also in Alsace and in Champagne, where, together with Pinot Noir and Chardonnay, it is used to make some of the sparkling wine for which that area is famous. This is a fairly vigorous variety and is not as particular about soil and site as Pinot Noir. Rootstocks such as 125AA or Kober 5BB should be chosen, except when the ground is rich; then it would be better to substitute SO4 or 5C. Pinot Meunier ripens its wood pretty well and therefore stands up to the rigours of winter.

This is another vine which must not be overcrowded. It responds to cane or spur pruning and should be given plenty of room if it is to succeed. The fruit ripens early enough to be considered suitable for cultivation in the United Kingdom, and the yield should be about the same as that of Pinot Noir, although the quality of the wine is not comparable.

Pinot Noir

All over the world the Pinot Noir or Blauer Spätburgunder is held in high esteem for its unrivalled quality. Claret lovers will no doubt rate the Bordeaux vine Cabernet Sauvignon as its peer but, like Riesling, the Burgundian grape has the ability to produce a delectable wine without the help of any other variety. By removing the skins before fermentation, it can also be used for the production of white wine and, together with Chardonnay and Pinot Meunier, forms the basis of Champagne. Apart from France, where it has been cultivated for centuries, Pinot Noir can be found in Germany, Austria, Switzerland and Italy. It has also been planted in some Communist countries, as well as in California, Australia, the Argentine, Chile and South Africa. It has already been tried in England, where, thanks to the lack of sun in our climate, it tends to produce a rosé wine; by dint of blending with a suitable variety, however, an adequate depth of colour might be achieved. Given a favourable site, it might be worth planting in this country but, as with Kerner and Schönburger, it could be difficult to ripen.

Some care should be taken to find a favourable site. The choice of soil is also important, for Pinot Noir is unlikely to thrive in cold, heavy soils of an impervious nature. The vineyard should be protected from the wind and able to gain the maximum benefit from the sun. In order to obtain the highest Oechsle reading, the soil should be warm and rich, light but reasonably moist and preferably with a sand or gravel structure.

The most suitable rootstock for this variety is SO4, but 5C, 5BB or 125AA can also be used; in acid soils 3309C is recommended. The growth potential is good, so the vines should be allowed enough room to develop freely. At least 5 feet 6 inches should be allowed between the rows and the vines trained to a height of 2 feet 6 inches, with two long, arching fruit canes.

The variety is not specially vulnerable to fungous diseases, but because of the tight bunch formation and fragile nature of the berries, adequate precautions must be taken to prevent botrytis from attacking the fruit. The wood ripens quite well and should overwinter without damage; in Britain the buds may escape the spring frosts by breaking on the late side.

Pinot Noir is a vine that has suffered some degeneration over the years, principally with respect to the yield. It is therefore important to obtain clonally selected stock if this variety is to be seriously considered. The research stations and institutions at Geisenheim, Weinsberg and Freiburg are able to supply this. The yield, if special clones are planted, may reach 5 tons per acre; otherwise it is unlikely to exceed 3 tons.

As already stated, Pinot Noir is rather too late for England. On the Continent it can show an Oechsle weight of 80° with an acidity of 0.6–0.8 per cent. To achieve anything approaching these figures, the fruit should be left as long as possible and harvested only when circumstances make it imperative. To do this without attracting botrytis, great attention should be paid to wide spacing and the free circulation of air.

Regner

Georg Scheu, the well-known plant breeder who was responsible for producing the very successful Scheurebe vine in addition to many other listed varieties, crossed the Gamay from Beaujolais with a white dessert grape called Luglienca Bianca in 1929. The result of this cross was the new cultivar Regner, named after a Fräulein Regner who worked for many years at the Alzey Institute.

So far this vine has not really been tested in the United Kingdom. Few growers have planted it, which is a pity because the variety has made a very promising start in the experimental vineyard at Wye College. It has much to commend it, as will be evident from the following details.

Regner prefers a well aerated soil and may not thrive as well on heavy clay; otherwise it is not too particular about soil or site. Strong vertical growth is a feature of this variety, and the new canes should be able to ripen without difficulty.

Although fairly resistant to downy mildew and dead arm disease, it can suffer from oidium and should therefore be given a little extra space in the vineyard. Rows should be 5 feet 6 inches apart, with 4 feet 6 inches between the plants. The vine can be allowed to carry up to ten buds per square yard. It does better than most when it comes to setting its fruit and is relatively free from stem rot. Regner is usually grafted on a vigorous rootstock such as 125AA, 5BB or 5C.

The fruit yields a must with an Oechsle weight similar to that of Müller-Thurgau and an acidity slightly lower. It ripens a few days earlier but is often harvested afterwards in order to obtain a higher gravity. The wine has an unobtrusive muscat flavour and is generally pleasant and well balanced.

Reichensteiner

A comparatively new cultivar from the Geisenheim Institute, Reichensteiner is likely to appeal to the English grower because it ripens early (about the same time as Müller-Thurgau) and yields a generous quantity of fruit with a good specific gravity. The grapes are produced in loose bunches and are therefore less vulnerable to the ravages of botrytis; it follows that the harvest can often be delayed, allowing a further increase in the must weight.

The vine was produced in 1939 from Müller-Thurgau and a cross between Madeleine Angevine and Calabreser-Fröhlich. It has been planted in the United Kingdom but does not meet with universal approval because the wine has a rather neutral flavour. Nevertheless, there are soils which can impart an individual character that is likely to appeal to the discerning palate.

Reichensteiner needs a fairly good soil and a frost-free site protected from the wind. It should be planted in rows not less than 5 feet apart with 4 feet 6 inches between the vines. A 2-foot trunk must be established with long fruiting canes, well arched if possible. The Pendelbogen method of training suits this variety and, as a rule, six to eight buds per square yard will be sufficient. The wood is a little reluctant to ripen.

Since Reichensteiner is not the most vigorous of vines, it is advisable to choose a strong rootstock. 5BB or 125AA is usually recommended, but in rich soil it is better to choose 5C.

Like Müller-Thurgau, the variety tends to suffer from downy and powdery mildew but is less likely to be attacked by botrytis, for the reasons already mentioned. Regular applications of fungicide are therefore necessary.

Reichensteiner can yield a must with a specific gravity up to 10° higher than that of Müller-Thurgau. The acidity may also be a fraction more pronounced. The two varieties therefore complement each other, and the wines made from them are frequently blended together.

Riesling

Although this famous variety ripens rather too late for the United Kingdom, this book would be incomplete if it were omitted, particularly as it has been planted in some of our vineyards. No one is really sure of its origin, although there are those who believe it to be a legacy of the Roman occupation; certainly it has been cultivated in the Rhineland for a very long time.

The correct name of the variety is Weisser Riesling (White Riesling) although there are many synonyms. Perhaps the most common of these are Rheinriesling, Johannisberger and Klingelberger. Some totally unconnected varieties have borrowed this famous name, presumably in order to promote their own image. Descriptions such as Welschriesling and Schwarzriesling (another name for Pinot Meunier) are in common use, whereas the title Riesling Silvaner, banned by the EEC as an alternative for Müller-Thurgau, is still permitted in Austria and the other countries. One synonym used for Riesling which may be of interest to the British is Hockheimer, derived from the village of Hockheim in the Rheingau, where Queen Victoria once owned a vineyard. Hence the word Hockamore, or Hock, for short, meaning any German white wine.

Although Riesling is a most accommodating vine in nearly every way, it needs a really good site. It is interesting to observe that in Germany, where they should know what they are doing, this variety is always given the best position. If there is a choice, Riesling is to be found in the warmest and most sheltered area.

This is partly because it happens to ripen late in the season and requires whatever benefits are available.

It follows therefore that growers in this country should chance their arm with Riesling only if they are in a position to provide the vine with the best sites that Britain can offer, perhaps in the South-West, on a south-facing slope and well away from the wet and windy areas. For the variety will grow on almost any soil, is able to withstand really cold winters and is resistant to all the common fungous diseases. It is susceptible only to brenner, stem rot and stem atrophy, but all these should be possible to control.

One way to reduce their incidence is to allow the vine some extra space. Not less than 5 feet 6 inches should separate the rows, and although the plants can be closer, even as little as 4 feet apart, in our rich English soil it may be better to allow more room.

The harvest yield is thought to be influenced by clone selection and is supposed to vary, under suitable conditions, from $3\frac{1}{2}$ to 6 tons per acre of vines. Much, however, will depend on the rootstock, which must be chosen with care. English growers should consider using 26G, which is less resistant to phylloxera but otherwise highly suitable. If this is not available, rootstocks 3309C, SO4, 5C or 125AA are to be recommended.

As already indicated, the climate in Great Britain does not favour the cultivation of this vine. In northern Germany conditions are also imperfect, yet the Riesling grape is to be found in profusion all along the banks of the Moselle and its tributaries. Sometimes the must weight fails to reach 50°Oechsle, but this marvellous variety can still be made to produce good wine. In addition, the Germans have found it possible to achieve by means of 'wet sugaring', a practice still permitted by the EEC, what is virtually a dilution of the must with water without materially affecting the flavour of the end product. This is important, because if the alternative measure did not exist, the natural acidity of the fruit could be too high, even in Germany, requiring for adjustment too generous an addition of calcium carbonate.

It is scarcely necessary to dwell on the unparalleled qualities of a really good Riesling wine as produced in the Moselle valley or the Rheingau. Perhaps it is worth observing that although the variety is also grown in France, Italy, Switzerland, Austria, America and South Africa, as well as in many other wine-producing countries, nowhere does it seem able to reach the same degree of perfection. German Riesling wines display a nobility of breeding and elegance. They are both flowery and fruity and are accompanied by a superb bouquet which is often considered to be reminiscent of ripe peaches. It would be fair to say that the Riesling vine is one of the aristocrats of the *Vitis vinifera* community.

Schönburger

Produced at the Geisenheim Institute by crossing Spätburgunder (Pinot Noir) with an Italian dessert variety known as Pirovano 1, which was itself made from a cross between Chasselas Rosa and Muscat Hamburg. The original name, Rosa Muskat, was disallowed as not being distinctive, so the variety has been described as Schönburger after a castle on the Rhine.

The vine has been planted in Somerset and Kent, somewhat optimistically perhaps, because it ripens rather late in the season. Growers speak well of its performance, however, for in both counties it has managed to produce surprisingly good wine.

Nevertheless, it would be unwise to plant this variety on a windy site, especially where the soil is cold, poor or unduly dry. It needs warmth and plenty of manure. Given the right conditions, it grows easily and is resistant to all fungous diseases. The young wood ripens well and is therefore able to stand up to the frosts of winter.

Schönburger should be grafted on to SO4 or 5C if the vineyard is fertile; on soils which are not quite so rich 125AA or 5BB might be preferable. The vine has a fairly vigorous upright growth and will respond to intensive planting at 4 feet apart, with 5 feet between the rows. It should be able to yield 4 tons per acre in Britain, with a higher specific gravity than Müller-Thurgau and a lower acidity if the fruit has an opportunity to ripen. The main stem should not be less than 2 feet high and does better if the fruiting canes are not arched. Ten buds per square yard should produce the best results.

The wine is reputed to develop a strange flavour on occasions, but so far, where it has been planted in the United Kingdom, the results have been very promising.

Seibel 13.053

The abundant yield that is often a feature of this variety has made Seibel 13.053 a popular vine with the English grower. Of additional appeal is the prospect of making a red or rosé wine, although care should be taken to ensure that the method of vinification adopted produces the best result.

Before he retired Dr Pollard of Long Ashton Research Station conducted some interesting experiments with this hybrid and came to the conclusion that fermentation on the skins was likely to produce an unpleasant flavour in the wine, although this would not occur if the skins were removed. Seibel 13.053 has a pigmented must and is able to yield a rosé wine of good colour if treated this way. Flash pasteurization of the must could, however, produce a palatable red wine, and experiments with this prolific hybrid should continue.

Seibel 13.053 was obtained by crossing Seibel 7042 with Seibel 4509. Its fruit ripens fairly early, at about the same time as that of Seyval Blanc; it is also equally vigorous and is inclined to produce a number of lateral shoots.

Septimer

Produced in 1927 at the Alzey Institute by Georg Scheu as a cross between Gewürztraminer and Müller-Thurgau. The variety has so far found little favour in Britain on account of its rather low yield; at best it is unlikely to produce more than 4 tons per acre. In addition, it is an easy victim to fungous diseases, even more vulnerable than Müller-Thurgau. Downy mildew, powdery mildew and botrytis cinerea can attack it unless a rigid pattern of leaf control is undertaken, and a winter spray of DNOC will be advisable for the control of phomopsis.

In spite of these failings, the variety ripens at the same time as Müller-Thurgau, with a higher Oechsle weight. In Rheinhessen it reaches an average of 90° and seldom fails to ripen fully. Like Müller-Thurgau, it has difficulty in ripening its wood and should never be planted in a frost pocket, although a later bud burst obviates any danger from spring frosts. It prefers a rich soil and should be given plenty of room in order to encourage air circulation. In England Septimer should be planted in rows at least 6 feet apart, with 5 feet between the plants. A stem measuring 2 feet 3 inches should be allowed to carry two long, arched fruiting canes bearing up to twelve buds per square yard.

The best rootstock for the variety is SO4, provided the soil is reasonably fertile. The must tends to have a low acidity and is often used for blending with a variety that has not managed to ripen its fruit completely.

Seyval Blanc

Seyval Blanc is a French hybrid which enjoyed some measure of success in France and could be found principally in the Loire valley. Hybrids do not find favour with the EEC and have long been rejected by the Germans, so it is doubtful whether the vine can still be cultivated for commercial purposes in France.

Originally known as Seyve-Villard 5.276 after the breeder, it was obtained by crossing Seibel 4995 with Seibel 4986. Generally accepted to be one of the best hybrids, it can frequently be made to produce a good wine, although some would find the flavour rather neutral. It has the merit of being the first variety to feature prominently in the post-war revival of English viticulture.

When Sir Guy Salisbury-Jones planned his vineyard at Hambledon, he decided to plant Seyval Blanc on the advice of his French friends, who felt that a hybrid vine might do better in our climate than any variety of *Vitis vinifera*. The decision may have been justified, for a modest inclusion of Müller-Thurgau proved to be a failure on the site and was subsequently grubbed.

Seyval Blanc, as it was officially described by the EEC, is a fairly vigorous variety which can usually be relied upon to provide a good yield. It ripens on the early side but could provide some awkward problems in a difficult year. In spite of its hardy nature and resistance to disease, it tends to be harvested in Britain with a limited specific gravity. Records have shown that the Oechsle weight of the must averages about 10° less than that of Müller-Thurgau, with a noticeably higher acidity. There is no 'foxy' taste.

Siegerrebe

The Sieger vine is the result of yet another successful experiment by Georg Scheu at the Alzey Research Institute in Rheinhessen. It was achieved by crossing Madeleine Angevine with Gewürztraminer in 1929. It is an early-ripening variety, producing a wine with a powerful bouquet and a strong flavour suitable for blending.

The yield from this variety is low, about 2 tons to the acre, and is very dependent on the weather at flowering time; should this be unfavourable, the bunches fail to set. The fruit ripens early and is particularly attractive to wasps. In a bad year the damage done by these pests can be considerable, for they encourage other insects such as bees and flies, all more than ready to share the feast.

Siegerrebe does best in a soil that is not too rich. If it grows too vigorously, it fails to set its fruit, so for that reason a rootstock like SO4 should be chosen instead of 5BB or 125AA. It also helps to give the vines more room; 6 feet between the rows, with the plants 5 feet apart, could help to improve the fruit set. An early bud burst makes the variety vulnerable to spring frosts.

If it is possible to keep both insects and birds at bay, the Sieger vine can achieve an impressive must weight. By delaying the harvest a reading of 85–100 °Oechsle can be reached, although this may not be possible if a spell of bad weather brings botrytis.

The wine, at best, is of exceptional quality with a powerful bouquet. It is rich in extract, with plenty of character, but is normally found rather overpowering unless it is blended with wine from another variety. A very small percentage of Sieger will enliven or enhance a wine of otherwise pedestrian quality. It is frequently blended with Müller-Thurgau to great effect.

Würzer

Würzer is yet another new cultivar produced by Georg Scheu at the Alzey plant-breeding station in Rheinhessen. It is a cross between Gewürztraminer and Müller-Thurgau. English growers would do well to consider planting this variety, which has so far suffered comparative neglect. Although it ripens its fruit a little later than Müller-Thurgau, the must is able to achieve a higher sugar content.

Würzer is choosy about soil and prefers it to be porous and fairly fertile. A strong rootstock like Kober 5BB or 125AA is recommended, so that the variety can make the best use of its natural vigour. The vines should be spaced at a distance of 4 feet 6 inches, in rows that are 5–6 feet apart. The fruiting canes should be at least 2 feet from the ground, and the buds should be limited to eight per square yard.

Like Müller-Thurgau, the variety must be protected from

fungous diseases, to which it is rather susceptible, but it is much better at ripening the wood that it has produced during the growing season. In Germany it has an average yield of 12 tons per hectare (5 tones per acre), a performance that should guarantee an adequate harvest in England.

The wine has a powerful bouquet and a muscat flavour; the style is associated with the Traminer grape, and the must is often used for blending or for conversion into Süss-Reserv. With the acidity a little higher than that of Müller-Thurgau, the wine should be endowed with better keeping qualities. Given the right site and a good season, Würzer should be able to provide a wine of considerable merit in the United Kingdom.

Appendix
Manufacturers and Suppliers

Artificial Windbreaks

Bridport Gundry Ltd, The Court, Bridport, Dorset DT2 3QU. Tel: Bridport (0308) 56666

Clovis Lande Associated Ltd, Gaza Trading Estate, Hildenborough, Kent TN11 8PL. Tel: Weald (073277) 588

Environment and Beach Control Ltd, 5 Pierrpont Street, Bath BA1 1LB. Tel: Bath (0225) 62547

Farmers and Growers Industries Ltd, Canterbury Road, Worthing, Sussex. Tel: Worthing (0903) 64411

Low Brothers and Company (Dundee) Ltd, P.O. Box 54, South Ward Road, Dundee DD1 9JA. Tel: Dundee (0382) 27311

Mallardworth Ltd, 10 Broad Ground Road, Lakeside Industrial Estate, Redditch, Worcestershire. Tel: Redditch (0527) 21018

Netlon Ltd, Kelly Street, Blackburn, Lancashire BB2 4PJ. Tel: Blackburn (0254) 62431

Papropack (Midlands) Ltd, Wedgnock Lane, Wedgnock Industrial Estates, Warwick. Tel: Warwick (0926) 46354

Roko Containers, Strella House, 34 Stoney Street, Nottingham NG1 1NB. Tel: Nottingham (0602) 53877

Bird Netting

Low Brothers and Company (Dundee) Ltd, PO Box 54, South Ward Road, Dundee DD1 9JA. Tel: Dundee (0382) 27311

Knowle Nets, 20 East Road, Bridport, Dorset. Tel: Bridport (0308) 24342

Netlon Ltd, Kelly Street, Blackburn, Lancashire BB2 4PJ. Tel: Blackburn (0254) 62431

Priory Vineyards, Lamberhurst, Tunbridge Wells, Kent TN3 8DS. Tel: Lamberhurst (0892) 890 286

Spraying Equipment

E. Allman & Co. Ltd, Birdham Road, Chichester, West Sussex
   PO20 7BT. Tel: Birdham (0243) 512348

Cooper Pegler & Co. Ltd, Victoria Road, Burgess Hill, Sussex
   RH15 9LA. Tel: Burgess Hill (044 46) 42526

Drake & Fletcher Ltd, Park Wood, Maidstone, Kent. Tel:
   Maidstone (0622) 55531

Evers & Wall Ltd, St George's Way, Bermuda Industrial Estates,
   Nuneaton, Warwickshire. Tel: Bondgate (020 364) 2054

B. Honess & Co., Great Cheveney House, Marden, Tonbridge,
   Kent. Tel: Maidstone (0622) 831334

Micron Sprayers Ltd, Three Mills, Bromyard, Herefordshire
   HR7 4HU. Tel: Bromyard (0885) 82357

Vineyard Tractors

Kubota Tractors (UK) Ltd, Hut Green, Whitley Bridge, North
   Yorkshire DN14 ORX. Tel: Whitley Bridge (0977) 661787

Lely Imports Ltd, Crosshall Road, St Neots, Huntingdon,
   Cambridgeshire. Tel: Huntingdon (0480) 217113

Olcope Ltd, Whiffler Road, Norwich. Tel: Norwich (0603) 45303

Miscellaneous

Dietz, Franz, & Co. Kom.-Ges., 6536 Langenlonsheim/Nahe,
   West Germany (Grafting wax for vines)

Heath Engineering Works (Horsmonden) Ltd, Horsmonden,
   Kent. Tel: Brenchley (089 272) 2226 (Max Tapener Tie Gun)

Heilemann, Friedrich, D-7840 Müllheim, Löfflergasse 4, West
   Germany (Plastic posts and wires for vineyards)

Hunter Wilson & Partners, Society Street, Maybole, Ayrshire,
   Scotland. Tel: Maybole (0655) 2369 (High-tensile wire trellis)

Stabernack-Verpackung, 6420 Lauterbach/Hessen, West Germany (Kartonagen for grafted vines)

United Continental Steels Ltd, Broadway House, 1 The Broadway, Hatfield, Hertfordshire AL9 5BG. Tel: Hatfield (070 72)
   68133 (Agents for French metal posts for vineyards)

Voest AG, 4010 Linz/Donau, Austria (Metal posts for vineyards)

Index